The Reality We Create

The Influence of Beliefs and Consciousness on Our Health and Longevity

---

By Warren L. Cargal, L. Ac

The Reality We Create: The Influence of Beliefs and Consciousness
on Our Health and Longevity

Cover Design by Anna Green

Edited by Kristi Dale Richard

Printed in the United States, First Edition

Copyright © 2018 by Warren Cargal

ISBN 978-1-7328100-0-6

BIG
BOOST
MEDIA
HOBOKEN, N.J.

CONTENTS

Acknowledgments

Writing this book wouldn't have been possible without the Internet and some of the great tools now available to make the research, organizing, and writing process easier. For those of you considering writing a book, I thought it may be helpful to share with you my approaches to research-gathering and writing. Hopefully this will make your journey easier, and, if someone has a more organized approach, please share it with me!

First, there's a great deal of quality research now available on the Web. Many full articles are available for free through open access, and others you may need to purchase. Managing your data and citations can take a lot of your time if you don't organize this process effectively. The tools I found most helpful are:

Kindle reader. If you're reading eBooks as research for your writing, consider a Kindle reader. You can purchase a Kindle tablet from Amazon for under $99, or you can download a free app onto your PC, Mac or mobile phone that allows you to read eBooks. All of my book reading is done on the Kindle reader, which allows text to be highlighted, notes to be added, and content to be exported with references.

Readcube.com. This is free, or you can upgrade to the professional version that offers more editing functionality. The issue this tool resolves very nicely is being able to read a research article, highlight text you want to save for a quote, and save the content with a corresponding reference. Additionally, it has functionality to do searches for recently published articles based on keywords you enter.

Mendeley.com is a free reference manager that connects to Readcube. It's a tool that allows you to collect all of your research references in a single, searchable interface. There are browser extensions that allow you to save articles directly into the Mendeley interface when doing Internet searches. Readcube's reference manager is a little wonky for my taste; however, Readcube does allow you to couple other citation managers to the program for a fairly seamless export. Mendeley is simple to use and has a tool that allows you to build a reference—for example, if you're reading a magazine article on an Internet site and want to reference it.

Without a doubt, you wouldn't have this book in your hands today if it weren't for the diligent work of Lynn Gray. Lynn has worked as a writer and editor for over 30 years and has published nine books. She's a long-time student of Buddhism and assisted with the editing of Culadasa's best-selling work, *The Mind Illuminated: A Complete Meditation Guide Integrating Buddhist Wisdom and Brain Science*, and Lama Shenpen Drolma's *Change of Heart: The Bodhisattva Peace Training of Chagdud Tulku.* Lynn has studied with Sogyal Rinpoche, Culadasa, and Lama Shenpen, and she believes the cultivation of mindfulness is the key to living compassionately. She has been my editor throughout this process of trying to explain that reality is nothing like we ordinarily take it to be and, furthermore, Buddhist philosophers knew the details of the quantum 'illusion-like' nature of reality at least two thousand years ago. She has helped me make this understandable and approachable.

I also want to acknowledge the works of Mae-Wan Ho, a geneticist who was known for her critical views on genetic engineering and evolution, and Rupert Sheldrake, an English author and researcher in the field of parapsychology.

I read Ho's first book, *The Rainbow and the Worm,* fifteen years ago. The book has stuck with me all these years because of her insights into molecular biology and the thermodynamics of living systems. She incorporates a wide range of discoveries in contemporary physics ranging from non-equilibrium thermodynamics to quantum optics as a lens through which to understand life, and she provides an exquisite view of biophysics.

Sheldrake's books have always been interesting to me because they exemplify a fundamental aspect of human nature, which is curiosity. Curiosity, after all, is just another name for scientific inquiry. His basic view is that science, at present, is limited by assumptions that restrict inquiry, and that there are major unsolved problems relating to consciousness, cosmology, and other areas of science. His books set forth hypotheses that can be tested and that could end centuries of dogmatic views and move us forward to new frontiers.

The work of Ho and Sheldrake has been instrumental in helping me to formulate many of the insights involved in molecular biology and quantum physics along with providing me with insight into the nature and function of reality. However, I need to make clear that the discussion in this book about current research in quantum physics and molecular biology represents my own understanding of these subjects.

When I began this project, my intention was to identify some of the potential interfaces between quantum physics and molecular biology, because current scientific views of thermodynamics leave significant energy deficits within biological systems. However, the work evolved into looking at the nature of reality and the parallels and interconnections between quantum physics and Buddhist philosophy to reveal an unconditioned dimension of our existence—our fundamental awareness.

In writing this book, I've dispensed with much of the nomenclature and definitions associated with quantum physics, the Buddhist tradition, and the psychology of consciousness. In the context of psychology, I didn't think it helpful to segment individual consciousness into an ego, higher self, or other psychological terms. Our awareness is comprised of both refined and unrefined aspects which we'll discuss in depth. My intent was to observe the components of consciousness without naming them.

Regarding the Buddhist tradition and God, I wanted to transcend the religious structures and beliefs. To this end, I didn't want to introduce a foreign set of terms, customs, or practices. My intent was to take the reader on a journey out of our limited and parochial views of reality toward an increasingly vast understanding of the structure of life and consciousness. To do this, I felt it was important to avoid coloring the journey with social, religious, or psychological views.

I hope this book will enjoy a wide readership. I believe the themes are pertinent to our personal health as well as that of a society deeply entrenched in dogmatic views that creates much suffering. For readers who have expertise in the areas I touch upon, I'd like to make clear that I haven't been able to cover every aspect of the relevant science, and you may identify areas that seem deficient. It's been a challenge to take the technical science and present it to a general audience. I had to make choices to exclude some details of quantum physics and molecular pathways to tell the story.

I also want to express my heartfelt gratitude to my teachers— John Pierrakos, MD; Barbara Ann Brennan; Vic Baranco; and Peter Fenner—for their guidance, love, and wisdom, which have enriched my life in more ways than I can express.

Special thanks also goes to my son, Collin. At the time this book was written, Collin was in his late teens and his favorite response to most questions was, "No." As a father, I was the proverbial diamond in the rough—someone with hidden, exceptional characteristics and/or future potential but who hadn't experienced the refining process which would make them truly stand out. Collin provided that polishing as I worked through the myriad ways and emotions of how to respond to "No."

Finally, this book wouldn't have been possible without the unwavering intellectual and emotional support of my beloved wife, Kimberly Cahill.

Warren L. Cargal

January 3, 2018

PART ONE: Chapter 1
The Knotty Problem

"I AM OZ.... the Great and Powerful!
Who are you?"

-The Wizard of Oz

This book is about extending one's lifespan and, during that extended lifespan, living a healthy life that's reflective of your true nature—that which is real and unconditioned by our beliefs and misconceptions. The approach presented in this book is based on the latest quantum physics research coupled with Buddhist meditation techniques that have been practiced and refined for over 2500 years. It's not only remarkable but timely that two of the most powerful avenues for exploring the nature of reality—quantum physics and meditation—lead to the same ground, and that ground is emptiness. But this is an emptiness filled with compassion and a deep caring for all sentient life and the world we inhabit.

When it comes to understanding emptiness, it's not necessary to attend workshops to "get it" nor are there any special nutraceuticals or herbal formulas which impart this understanding. Essentially, all that's required is reading this book and—get ready, here it comes—twenty minutes a day of your time. But here's the hard part: For those twenty minutes, you sit quietly.

First, here's a little background on how this book unfolded. In Traditional Chinese Medicine, there's a diagnostic concept called the "knotty problem," which takes into account the complex interconnections of different causes and symptoms in a disease process. A way to imagine this is ball of twine all knotted up.

The Reality We Create

Sometimes a patient will present with numerous symptoms, and the task for the practitioner is to tease out the knots to identify an underlying cause while treating the symptoms. This means that if the underlying issue isn't addressed, treating symptoms could exacerbate the problem.

After writing my first book, I found myself dealing with three knotty problems, which led to my writing this book. Here's how the first problem played out: One day, a couple of months after I finished the first book, *Your Mitochondria—Key to Health and Longevity*, I was pedaling along on my bike (I often get creative insights when I'm biking) and I started thinking about the energy that's produced by the mitochondrial electron-transport chain.

This is an electrochemical energy in which electrons are transferred from a donor molecule to an acceptor molecule. The energy produced is used by the body to drive its myriad physiological processes such as thinking, vision, heartbeat, and muscular movement. These chemical reactions are well defined by chemical kinetics and are rate-limited, meaning they can only occur as fast as the slowest step in the process.

As I was rounding a corner on the bike, I saw a tree limb in my path and braked immediately. I stopped myself without a crash, unclipped my shoes from the pedals, and stood with my feet on the ground, surveying the tree limb. At that moment, I had a profound insight.

The actions involved in my avoiding the crash were way outside normal biochemical reactions and energy-transfer processes. And I don't mean just slightly outside of normal boundaries, I mean WAY outside—probably at the speed of light or maybe even instantaneous.

Let's look at one aspect of my revelation so you can understand the implications. Focusing on just the visual part of the process, I rounded the corner and saw the tree limb. The phenomenon of vision is instantaneous and stereoscopic (meaning we perceive depth) and, most importantly, there's no delay (not even of a microsecond) as would be indicated by electrochemical energy transfer. In other words, the speed at which impulses travel down the nerves and through nerve junctions from the eye to the brain, to form a coherent image, doesn't happen at the speed required for instantaneous vision.

The First Knotty Problem

This is how my first knotty problem evolved, and I just couldn't shake it. My view of the world has been based on the scientific claim that all reality is material (physical). There's no reality but material reality, and consciousness is a by-product of the physical activity of the brain.

This scientific view of nature as matter obeying laws of physics is so compelling that we easily forget everything we know of the objective world is by way of human consciousness. This subjective world of matter is our only reality.

The bicycle incident identified a gaping void in my concept of reality, which the grandeur and omnipotence of science wasn't going to be able to fill. It was like the scene in "The Wizard of Oz" when Dorothy meets the grand and powerful Oz and asks him who the man behind the curtain is. Oz responds, "Pay no attention to that man behind the curtain! The Great Oz has spoken!"

In my first book, I identified how our mitochondria can drive the age-related diseases of cardiovascular dysfunction, diabetes, arthritis, neurodegeneration, cancer, and premature aging. The progression of these diseases is influenced by compromised mitochondrial energy production.

I suggest three, simple, fundamental protocols, along with nutritional approaches, that are supportive of enhanced mitochondrial energy production to augment one's overall health and longevity. The three fundamental protocols are:

1. Deep breathing—as opposed to shallow breathing, because mitochondria need oxygen for energy production
2. A reduction in the number of calories consumed along with avoiding sugars and carbohydrates
3. Mild exercise to drive mitochondrial biogenesis

In this book, *The Reality We Create,* the focus is on energy moving at the quantum level within the body coupled with our consciousness. This is another level of the process to improve our health and extend our longevity. This book explores breathtaking discoveries about the holes in our view of reality that profoundly affect our life and health.

It's written for the reader who has little or no familiarity with today's physics, but is curious to find out what we know, as well as what we don't yet understand about our lives and the world we live in. Its purpose is to expand the definition of a healthier and longer life to include a life of greater authenticity, compassion, and love for yourself and everything in our world.

Let me give an example of one particularly challenging problem that science is still trying to sort out: How is it possible to almost instantaneously call up a memory in detail?

This is considered a knotty problem because electrical pulses in the brain move at a maximum speed of 120 mps (miles per second). This velocity could, perhaps, be adequate to account for some of the involuntary functions inside the human body but certainly isn't adequate to account for the speed of human activities that involve computing, recalling memories, vision, emotional responses, and other functions of the mind.

The similarities between computer circuits and brain cells have driven brain researchers to construct computer models to imitate the workings of the brain. Initially, they tried serial computers, and then, to account for speed, parallel computers came into play. Today, computer models dominate most brain research but are still far from duplicating the functions of the human brain.

This brings us to the elusive relationship between the body and the mind. The brain-mind relationship has baffled mankind for a very long time. One main reason for this is that consciousness wasn't considered a candidate for scientific study until recently.

Many scientific studies indicate that mental phenomena—such as subjectively experienced desires, thoughts, emotions, and memories—influence brain function and behavior. In response to this empirical evidence, a growing number of cognitive scientists have concluded that mental phenomena are real, but they insist that in order to causally interact with the brain, the mind must be based in the physical. [1]

While physicists and biologists have devised highly sophisticated means of directly observing physical processes in living organisms, cognitive scientists have failed to develop rigorous ways of directly observing mental phenomena. This exclusion, or at least marginalization, of subjectively experienced mental events from objective observation has resulted in a "blind spot" in the scientific view of reality. [2]

The Second Knotty Problem

Once I began to investigate these blind spots—such as the fact that more energy is being produced in the body than can be accounted for by simple thermodynamics—I ran into the next knotty problem, which was just as perplexing.

If we want to investigate events occurring at the speed of light, quantum physics is the place to start. Here, we examine the elementary structure of the world, generated by a swarm of quantum events in which time and space don't exist. Quantum fields draw together space, time, matter, and light, exchanging information between one event and another. Reality is a network of granular events; the dynamic that connects them is probabilistic—between one event and another, space, time, matter, and energy melt into a cloud of probability. [3]

This is how the second problem unfolded: At the atomic level, events are interconnected and probabilistic. You may recall seeing a bell curve in a math or biology class. At the top of the curve, there's a 100% probability that an event will occur. On either side of this point, that probability declines as the points on the curve approach the baseline. This decline in probability is known as the collapse of the wave function, and you'll see this term used repeatedly throughout this book.

All of this doesn't seem too problematic until we consider what's been known by physicists for the last 90 years: This collapse of the wave function is brought about by an observer. No one yet knows how this transition from a mathematical abstraction of probability to its manifestation in concrete reality takes place, but, in some way, the observer—the person who designs and conducts these quantum field experiments—plays a key role in bringing the quantum world to life.

Your first thought may be that this is a world of the infinitely small—the world of electrons, protons, and atoms—which seems to have little effect in our lives. Oh, but it does, because we and everything in our universe is composed of these infinitely small particles and held together by electromagnetic forces. So, the second knotty problem is the collapse of the wave function resulting from the influence of an observer and the resultant unfoldment of reality.

What this points to is that science may have (inadvertently) encountered consciousness and that consciousness (the observer) may play a crucial role in the formation and evolution of the universe as we know it. When the ideas of quantum physics are viewed from the perspective of the way our everyday world appears—as one of solid matter and discrete objects—quantum concepts seem like an illusion. Yet, within the scientific community, there's a group that insists that ultimate reality is the ground under our feet, and consciousness is the illusion.

For example, most researchers in psychology and brain science regard consciousness as nothing more than an inherent and discrete aspect of the functioning of our individual brains—with no significance for the universe at large. As regards quantum physics, there can be no reasonable doubt that quantum events occur and are effective in the warm and wet environment of biological systems—including the brain. However, there's ongoing debate about whether these quantum events are correlated with mental activity and consciousness. The question becomes, how do we measure or quantify something we're a part of?

The quantum viewpoint now emerging is that consciousness—which is the fundamental substrate of reality—creates the "stuff" of the material world. [4] Essentially, the everyday reality of the solid world becomes the stuff of dreams and smoke at the quantum level, and the "observer" that creates the collapse of the waveform is consciousness.

The Third Knotty Problem

Graham Smelham, in his book, *Quantum Physics,* identified my third knotty problem thusly: "What a remarkable state of affairs; the manifestation of the solidity of the everyday world requires an essential lack of solidity at the quantum level, a lack of solidity which bears the hallmark of neither existence or non-existence nor both nor neither; how remarkable it also is that two thousand five hundred years ago, Buddhist philosophy pointed to the same insubstantial nature of reality." [5]

The teachings of Buddhism are based entirely on experience, including 2500 years of experience with meditation, focusing on and exploring the inner landscape of consciousness in the same quest for understanding as that of physicists exploring the quantum world today. Buddhism is a philosophy that has been honed and broadened over the millennia to provide guidance for exploring our consciousness. The practice of meditation brings us to a place of greater freedom, health, luminosity, and compassion.

The nature of the third knotty problem was that what had initially started out as an exploration to identify missing energy had evolved and, in fact, was pointing to how consciousness affects our health and every aspect of our life. I was given the clue that chasing after happiness by accumulating material goods and experiences provides no lasting happiness or security and, most importantly, doesn't nourish our life. Paradoxically, only the experience of emptiness can do this, and that's what we'll be discussing at length in the later chapters of this book.

In the last century, the human lifespan has reached documented lengths of over 120 years, meaning that life after 50 could be the bulk of our lifespan, and viewing our life through the lens of this possible longevity may be the most important decision we make, because we want this long life to be one of health and meaning. At the core of this longevity are dietary choices which nourish our physical body, and of equal importance, the care and feeding of our mind. If we're caught in repetitive loops of nonproductive or even harmful thoughts, our health and our quality of life are limited.

This book presents some of the tools that have been out there for a very long time which we can use to fundamentally improve our physical, emotional, and spiritual life.

Individuals concerned about healthy aging should understand that aging isn't fundamentally about superficial appearance but, rather, our appearance mirrors our conscious awareness and cellular maintenance throughout our life. As each of us thinks about our health maintenance as we get older, we need to examine our consciousness—which includes our beliefs and misconceptions.

When using meditation and mindfulness to view ourselves and our world, we become our authentic self. As a bonus, we'll look good for our age—youthful and not artificially young—and our health and vitality will be evident to all around us. The first step in adopting an individualized protocol of anti-aging—or, rather, healthy longevity—is to become educated about the science of our bodies and minds, which is the intent of this book.

The following are brief glimpses into what you'll find in the chapters ahead:

Chapter 2: Deconstructing Our Worldview – Most people are unconscious of the myths, allegories, and beliefs that shape their individual and social lives. This is largely because these beliefs are implicit rather than explicit, and they're powerful because they're unconscious and habitual. Because they're unconscious, we don't question them, and, insofar as they're collective—i.e., shared by our community and our culture— there's no incentive to question them. We will explore five of these beliefs and how they affect our lives.

Chapter 3: Biology and Beliefs – Each individual is a collection of traits programmed by the genes inherited from his or her parents. This is our genetic makeup. It's what we begin with, but it doesn't define who we are. Genes only code for protein expression and aren't a blueprint for how the body functions. Our bodies and our thoughts are in a state of flux from the moment we're born. We can influence some of these changes— not all, but a lot—by what we eat, what we do, and what we think. However, even more important to our well-being and health than these conscious choices and attitudes is the power of our subconscious.

Chapter 4: The Quantum World – We will explore how quantum theory has opened the door to a profoundly new vision of the world in which the observer, the observed, and the act of observation are fundamentally interlocked. As such, the very large, the very small, the very near, and the very far are interconnected.

Chapter 5: The Quantum Body – We will build on what we learned in Chapter 2 which revealed more energy is being produced in the body than can be accounted for by simple thermodynamics (food + water + oxygen in *and* work + heat loss + waste material out). We will examine where that surplus energy is coming from and how the body produces it.

Chapter 6: Spiritual Tradition-Consciousness – What we're able to experience with our senses seems real to us, but we're unable to perceive most of what's out there. We're swimming in a vast ocean of waves and frequencies. The mechanism by which these waves and frequencies are conjured into sticks and stones is our consciousness. We will discuss the nature of consciousness, who or what is conscious, and learn about the Four Noble Truths.

Chapter 7: The Practice – We will investigate a practice for observing our thoughts as they manifest. By observing our thoughts, we begin to "see" what we're creating. Some of these thoughts and patterns aren't supportive in helping us to have a creative, healthy, and long life. As part of this practice, we'll explore ways to gently deconstruct thought-forms that reinforce our belief that we're separate from the sea of consciousness in which we exist.

Chapter 8: Deepening the Experience – We will learn about an approach to deepen the meditation experience. All that's required is awareness of each thought, image, or belief as it manifests in our consciousness without judgment, because judgment conditions our mental space. It's sufficient to simply observe and acknowledge these patterns, meaning they don't require fixing.

Chapter 9: Deconstructing Our Conditioned Views – I present an approach infused with the rich legacy of Buddhist meditation practices that will help to dismantle some of the thick overlay of mental structures which prevent us from moving into greater openness in our life—bringing us to a life in which our experience is freer of feelings, thoughts, perceptions, and interpretations that limit our life and cause us a good deal of suffering.

Chapter 10: The Mystery – To learn anything, it's necessary to have the courage to accept that what we think we know—including our most rooted convictions—may be wrong. As I began my investigations–which incorporated meditation and inquiry–a different worldview began to emerge for me, one that demonstrated the interrelationship and interdependence of all sentient beings on our planet. What started out as an investigation into energy flow within the body morphed into revealing how our beliefs influence not only our behavior but how our lives—including our health, longevity, and creativity—unfold.

References:

1. Wallace, B. Alan. Hidden Dimensions: The Unification of Physics and Consciousness (Columbia Series in Science and Religion). Columbia University Press. Chap 1, Kindle Edition.
2. Ibid.
3. Rovelli, Carlo. Reality Is Not What It Seems: The Journey to Quantum Gravity. Penguin Publishing Group. Chap 1, Kindle Edition.
4. Graham Smethan. Quantum Buddhism: Dancing in Emptiness - Reality Revealed at the Interface of Quantum Physics & Buddhist Philosophy (Chap 1, Kindle). Lulu.com
4. Ibid., Chap 3.

Chapter 2
Deconstructing Our Worldview

The Question is what is The Question? Is it all a Magic Show? Is Reality an Illusion? What is the framework of The Machine? Darwin's Puzzle: Natural Selection? Where does Space-Time come from? Is there any answer except that it comes from consciousness? What is Out There? T'is Ourselves? Or, is IT all just a Magic Show? Einstein told me: "If you would learn, teach!"

-John Wheeler, American Physicist

Most people are unconscious of the myths, allegories, and assumptions that shape their individual and social lives. This is largely because these beliefs are implicit rather than explicit, and they're powerful because they're unconscious and habitual. Because they're unconscious, we don't question them, and, insofar as they're collective—i.e., shared by our community and our culture—there's no incentive to question them.

Rupert Sheldrake, in his book, *Science Set Free: 10 Paths to New Discovery,* argues that our life is held back by assumptions that have been held for so long that they have become dogmas. By held back, he means our life would be improved without these mental constraints. It would be freer, healthier, and more creative. [1]

The biggest delusion many people hold is that science knows—or will discover—all the answers. In principle, the fundamental questions of life are already understood through science, and now science is focused on the details. The underlying hypothesis for contemporary science is that reality is material or physical. Full stop – Reality can only be material reality. According to the scientific argument, consciousness is simply a by-product of the brain's normal mechanisms. Matter is unconscious. Evolution is purposeless. [2]

Here are five core beliefs (beliefs, mind you, not truths) that may be operating in your everyday life. After the explanation of each core belief, I pose a couple of questions to help you examine the belief in the spirit of beginning an inquiry rather than as an unquestioned truth.

ONE: Classical physics explains what we are and what we do.

Classical physics was initiated by Isaac Newton in the 1600s and was later enhanced and, in some cases, contradicted by the work of James Clerk Maxwell, Albert Einstein, and others. Classical physics is any previous theory predating theories that are newer, more complete, or more widely applicable. When a theory is introduced and accepted, it is considered "modern". If this new "modern" theory completely changed the way we understand physics, the older theories and the theories based on the previously accepted principle, would be considered "classical' physics. Categories of classical physics include Newton's laws of motion, Maxwell's equations (classical electrodynamics), classical thermodynamics, special relativity and general relativity, and classical chaos theory and nonlinear dynamics. "Modern" physics generally refers to quantum mechanics, in particular quantum theory and relativity. [3]

Classical physics is built on the theory that all objects are composed of particles, which move in accordance with mathematical laws. As a deterministic theory, classical physics relies on the belief that the "state of the physical world at any time is completely determined by the state at any earlier time." [4]

Classical physics is deterministic. The entire physical world is determined by what the physical world was at a previous time. From the first moment the universe began, the interactions between tiny component parts has determined every state of the physical world throughout history. [5]

Following this argument, classical physics describes a human being as a "mechanical automaton"; that is, every aspect of our behavior is predetermined prior to our birth solely by the mechanical interactions among molecules and atoms. Similar to the state of the physical world, our mental processes are solely based on mechanical conditions—without influence from our thoughts, feelings, ideas, or intentions. Many people would say that their conscious intentions are a driving factor in how they make a decision. Based on the principles of classical physics, this intuitive sense is an illusion. In other words, thoughts and feelings are just byproducts of our brain activity that have no effect on our motivations or actions. [6]

"Consciousness is at all times primarily a selecting agency. It is present when choices must be made between different possible courses of action." [7] If feelings truly have no influence on physical action, why are pleasure and psychological pain so closely related to good and harmful actions respectively?

This scientific view of Nature as matter which obeys laws of physics is so compelling that we easily forget that everything we know of the objective world is by way of our consciousness. Reality is no more than our perception of it.

However, Albert Einstein upended many of the classical physics theories with the discovery of quantum physics (also called quantum mechanics), which moved our understanding of the universe from one of physical constructs with fixed characteristics, functions, and behaviors to one based entirely on energy—energy in the form of waves and particles that are continuously influenced by other, often invisible forces, such as gravity. Stated very simply, classical physics is built on theorems derived from observation. Newton's famous example of the falling apple is a classic example of the origin of classical physics.

Quantum physics, on the other hand, is largely based on invisible forces and deals with the world on a micro level. That's a good way to generally divide the two—classical physics deals with macro interactions and quantum physics is concerned with micro interactions. There are essentially three ways quantum mechanics differs from classical physics. First, quantization is often used to make energy, momentum, and other variables limited to discrete values. Secondly, objects have particle characteristics and wave characteristics. Thirdly, the quantities measured in quantum physics are limited by their lack of precision. [8] The emphasis in quantum physics is on energy—objects and phenomena that often can't be observed, even with the most powerful microscopes, and can only be explained mathematically. In other words, when the world is described on the quantum level, it becomes a whole lot more mysterious, and a whole lot more fluid.

However, a conventional view of physics argues that the principles of quantum mechanics which govern wave-particle interactions only apply at the level of atoms and don't apply to our consciousness. This view—which, until recently, was held by most physicists—assumes that Nature is divided into the classical world of everyday objects—in which Newton's laws of mechanics hold—and the mysterious world of quantum systems at the scale of elementary particles, atoms, and simple molecules. In this world, what appear to be things are both wave and particle and can be in two places or in multiple, contradictory states at the same time. [9]

Questions:

- Do you think of yourself as a genetically programmed machine in a mechanical universe? Probably not. Most of us feel ourselves to be fluid beings interacting with a living, evolving world.

- If you don't believe you're an automaton living in a mechanical world, how do you see yourself?

TWO: Our genetics defines who we are, how healthy we are, and how long we live.

My uncles and aunts would always tell me how much I looked like my dad. I was, "a chip off the old block," they'd say. Although they didn't know it, they were making a statement about genetics.

Genetics is now at the center of our view of biology. Hereditary information is coded in genes, and the words "hereditary" and "genetic" are seen as equivalent terms and often used interchangeably. The double-helix model of deoxyribonucleic acid (DNA) was discovered in 1953. With this discovery, it looked like heredity would soon be completely understood on a molecular basis. It seemed clear that DNA is a molecule that carries the genetic instructions for growth, development, functioning, and reproduction in all living organisms. In 2000, the Human Genome Project succeeded in defining the sequence of human DNA—i.e., the human genome [9]. It seemed everything about genetics in humans could now be explained.

As Sheldrake points out in his book, *Science Set Free: 10 Paths to New Discovery*, "This astonishing achievement of sequencing the human genome has indeed transformed our view of ourselves, but not as anticipated. The first surprise was that there were so few genes. Rather than the predicted 100,000 or more, the final tally of about 23,000 was very puzzling, and all the more so when compared with the genomes of other animals much simpler than ourselves. There are about 17,000 genes in a fruit fly, and about 26,000 in a sea urchin. Many species of plants have far more genes than us—rice has about 38,000, for example." [9]

We've since learned that DNA doesn't determine the particular structures or activities of organisms. Most genes code for the amino acid sequences that will form polypeptide chains, which will form protein molecules. In turn, these protein molecules will influence how a cell is organized and it behaves. Some genes don't make proteins, but instead control the protein synthesis process. DNA is just part of this process, not the dictator. Genes are simply plans for a certain characteristic or instinct, and, as we know, plans are influenced by many things in life. If pressed, biologists will say genes only determine the amino acid sequence for proteins or control protein synthesis. [9,11]

What this means is that there's no blueprint for the structure and function of organisms. Knowing the DNA of an ant or a human being doesn't tell us everything about the specifics of an individual bug or person. There's a big leap from an individual's gene sequence and how these sequences are exhibited in that individual. [10]

Recently, so-called "genome-wide association studies" compared 30,000 genomes of people to see how height is inherited. They were able to identify about fifty genes associated with being tall or short. Surprisingly, however, only about 5 percent of height inheritance could be accounted for by the identified genes. This means that 95% of height heritability was unaccounted for by these genes. [11]

There have been many other examples of "missing heritability," including the heritability of a number of diseases. As a result, the value of personal genomics in determining the risk factors for illness in a particular person is questionable. In 2009, twenty-seven leading geneticists published a paper in Nature discussing the missing heritability of complex diseases. One of the authors was Francis Collins, who at one point led the Human Genome Project. At that point in time, there had been over 700 publications on genome-scanning, costing over $100 billion. The researchers recognized that despite the considerable amount of time and resources that had gone into these studies, geneticists only had a small understanding of how genetics influences disease. [12]

Nonetheless, most of us still believe—and, in some cases, rightly so—that our genes determine or at least influence our health. There's no doubt that if a woman's mother and grandmother had breast cancer, she's at a higher risk than a woman who has no history of breast cancer in her family. However, our genetic *predisposition* is only that—a predisposition. It neither guarantees nor threatens our physical or mental health. [13]

Of course, there's no doubt that some diseases – Huntington's chorea, beta thalasemmia, and cystic fibrosis, to name a few – can be traced to one faulty gene. However, these single-gene disorders are rare, affecting less than two percent of the population. Most people in the world have genes which allow them to survive and thrive. [14]

Millions of people mistakenly blame their poor health solely on "bad genes," instead of investigating the lifestyle, environmental, mental, and emotional factors that influence health. The truth is—much evidence has been gathered over the past couple of decades proving that all organisms—from the simplest plants to the most advanced mammals—acquire characteristics as they interact with their environment, and *these characteristics are passed on to their offspring.* Read that sentence again. You *are not* your genetic programming.

The study of the processes by which environmental factors—including thoughts, beliefs, and emotions—influence cells to generate heritable characteristics—without changing the DNA—and transmit them to future generations is called epigenetics. We'll talk about epigenetics at length in Chapter 3.

So, the question is—what activates genes? In 1990, H.F. Nijhout answered this in a paper titled "Metaphors and the Role of Genes and Development." Nijhout argues that scientists have wholly accepted the idea that genes completely control our biology. Scientists have heard this idea repeated for long enough that they forget it is a hypothesis, which hasn't been proven. The most recent scientific research even undermines the idea that our genes control so much. Nijhout proposes that people simply want to think that genetic engineering can not only cure diseases but prevent them and tailor our DNA to include more geniuses like Einstein and Mozart. So, the question remains, what activates genes? Nijhout concludes: "When a gene product is needed, a signal from its environment, not an emergent property of the gene itself, activates expression of that gene." So instead of thinking of genetics controlling health, remember, "It's the environment, stupid." [15]

Questions:

- Do you sometimes find yourself making statements that confirm your belief in the infallibility of genetics? Statements such as "I have diabetes because my mother and grandmother had it," or "My back is bad because my father always had problems with his back."

- How much do you think the environment you grew up in has affected who you are now, including your health?

THREE: Our memories reside in our brain.

Ah, memories. Those are some mysterious things, huh? Why do we remember a scene in our life from decades ago so vividly when we may not remember what we had for lunch yesterday? How does memory work? Where do our memories reside?

Most of us believe memories are embedded in places in our brains, like knick-knacks we've stuck into drawers and forgotten. If we believe our consciousness resides entirely in the physical confines of our gray matter, we probably never questioned that memories were anything more than neuronal traces in our brain.

Steven Rose is a neuroscientist who has explained the standard assumption about memories and where they reside as follows: "Memories are, in some way, 'in' the mind, and, therefore, for a biologist, also 'in' the brain. But how? The term 'memory' must include at least two separate processes. It must involve, on the one hand, that of learning something new about the world around us; and, on the other, at some later date, recalling or remembering that thing. We infer that what lies between the learning and the remembering must be some permanent record, a memory trace, within the brain." [16]

This "trace theory" may seem like a reasonable explanation, but it has serious logical issues. First of all, nobody's been able to look at a brain and find a memory trace, even after a century of trying to do so at a cost of billions of dollars. It's not like looking at the cracks of a cement foundation in your house and deducting what might have caused them. [17]

Here's another problem: In order for a memory trace to be activated, a retrieval system is necessary, and this system needs to be able to identify the stored memory it's looking for. This means the retrieval system must itself have a memory, or it wouldn't know what it's looking for. You see the pattern—the retrieval system requires a memory store that requires a retrieval system with memory, and so on, ad infinitum. [17]

There's a structural problem, too, because memories can persist for decades despite ongoing changes in the molecules of the brain. Francis Crick stated, "Almost all the molecules in our bodies—with the exception of DNA, the genetic material—turn over in a matter of days, weeks, or, at the most, a few months. How, then, is memory stored in the brain so that its trace is relatively immune to molecular turnover?" [17]

Consider that our brains may be more like radio or television receivers than hard-drive recorders. What we see on our brain's television screen at any given moment depends on how your receiver is tuned in to invisible fields. If you wanted to know what programs you watched yesterday, you couldn't analyze the receiver's hardware to find evidence of what you watched. [19]

In the same way, brain injuries and degeneration of brain tissue, as in Alzheimer's disease, that lead to loss of memory don't prove that these memories were stored in the damaged tissue. Disconnecting your flat-screen TV from the satellite dish, which causes the screen to go black except for a message letting you know "the signal has been lost," doesn't mean that signal is in the cable connecting the satellite to the screen. All the broadcasting is still being sent; it's just not being received and perceived by our conscious mind. [18]

Karl Pribram the late professor of psychology and psychiatry at Georgetown University, is best known to the public for his work in cognitive function and neurological research. He researched memory, emotion, motivation, and consciousness, and developed the holonomic brain model of cognitive function. Dr. Pribram proposed that holographic wave patterns aren't stored in the brain at all. He thought of the brain as a "waveform analyzer" rather than a storage system, comparing it to a radio receiver that picks up waveforms from the "implicate order" and rendering them explicit. This aspect of his thinking was influenced by the quantum physicist David Bohm, who suggested that the entire universe is holographic in the sense that wholeness is enfolded into every part. [18]

Pribram's hypothesis that memory is a resonant phenomenon where past brain activity affects similar patterns in the present. This is supported by scientists' inability to find physical traces of memory in the brain. Collective memory is dependent on resonance, just like individual memory, but the self-resonance based on an individual's own past is more specific and therefore more compelling. [18]

Questions:

- Do you believe memories are stored as material traces in our brains? If so, how do you think memory-retrieval systems in our brains recognize the memories they're trying to retrieve from our memory stores?

- If you don't think memories reside as material traces in the brain, where are they located?

FOUR: Our consciousness resides in our brain and is a product of our brain.

Most of us who were brought up as good little scientists have difficulty accepting that thoughts—specifically intentionality—can truly influence physical outcomes, particularly at a distance. You may recall Einstein's "spooky actions at a distance" theorems. In physics, "action at a distance" means an object doesn't have to make physical contact with another object to be moved, changed, or affected in some way. [20] This has been extended to include electrons on opposite sides of the universe. If an electron on one side of the universe changes the direction of its rotation, it can affect the rotation of an electron on the opposite side of the universe.

An offshoot of this concept is the "butterfly effect." This is an aspect of chaos theory that describes how important initial states are. In a deterministic, nonlinear system, even a small change to one state can lead to major changes in later states. The term was coined by mathematician, meteorologist, and pioneer of chaos theory Edward Lorenz.

The butterfly effect is derived from the metaphorical example of how a tornado's path and time of formation are affected by small influences, like a faraway butterfly flapping its wings months earlier. In other words, a very small action (generation of energy) from far away can have a powerful influence. Our thoughts and intentions are comprised of energy and may, therefore, be regarded as such an action. The power of thought and intention has been observed anecdotally for centuries, but only in recent decades has it been subjected to scientific scrutiny. [21]

Of course, we know the brain is a thing—a physical, living organism. The classical science explanation of the structure of and mechanism of operation in the brain can be found in most medical or biology textbooks. On average the brain is 1.3 kg. of gray matter comprising hundreds of billions of specialized cells known as neurons. These cells have electrical properties similar to computer circuits which are interconnected to each other and transmit signals. There are trillions of neuron-neuron connections in the brain. Just as in computer circuits, electrical signals are transmitted via neurons by unidirectional electrical pulses—which are excited, modulated, or inhibited by pulses in other neurons. [22]

Despite these similarities between the functions of our brains and those of computer circuits, the brain is not a "meat computer," as some people colorfully refer to it. In a computer circuit, electrical pulses are transmitted by the movement of electrons at an enormous velocity—half the speed of light. The electrical pulses in neurons, on the other hand, are transmitted by the movement of ions through neurons. Ions are much heavier than electrons. Even at their maximum speed, they can only move at 120 meters per second (mps). This speed isn't fast enough to account for the speed of human actions. Ions are much heavier than electrons and move through interneuron links established through biochemical junctions. In transistor circuits, all connections are exclusively electrical—nothing biochemical goes on in your computer, for which you can probably be grateful, else it be even more obstinate and willful than it already seems to be. [22]

Anyway, back to that bit about ions moving too slowly to account for how fast humans react. The maximum speed of 120 mps for neuronal electrical pulses may be adequate to account for some of the involuntary functions of the human body, but, according to quantum physics, this rate of speed is far too slow to support activities that involve the mind.

When attempting to understand consciousness, researchers have tried to understand it in terms of the relationship between the brain and the mind. So-called reductionists consider the two to be identical—with the mind representing the sum total of the activity in the brain. In the next chapter, we'll discuss, in depth, what consciousness is and where it resides.

Interestingly, essentially all efforts to understand the brain's functional activity have been based implicitly on certain principles of classical physics that have been acknowledged as fundamentally false for nearly a century. As mentioned previously, the classical understanding of nature explains all causal connections among anything we observe in terms of how material entities interact with one another, even though it's now universally accepted that each of our individual brains interprets signals from our senses and creates images in our brain that form our unique perception of reality.

Why this obstinance among scientists in admitting the true source of our health and longevity? Some believe this is a result of an all-too-common motivator in our world—greed. If we truly believed we could heal ourselves through knowledge of the true influences on our health, that would mean less business for physicians, pharmaceutical companies, and health insurers. It's long been observed in rigorously conducted clinical trials involving double-blind studies in which half the participants in the trials receive the drug being tested and half receive placebo ("sugar pills"), that many who received placebo showed improvement comparable to the people who received engineered chemical cocktails. [23] It's clear the power of the so-called "placebo effect" isn't an occasional artifact of these trials. There's something going on here that's real.

Questions:

- Do you believe your consciousness is merely an aspect of the activity of your brain? Is your perception of the material world—and the value you place on it— determined by unconscious processes in your brain rather than reason, evidence, and choice?

- Do you believe your consciousness and life experiences reside in your brain? If not, where does consciousness reside?

FIVE: The food we eat creates the energy for our body.

Many of us, myself included, grew up in a "clean your plate" family and we received many mixed messages around food and eating. We can see how this has played out in our society, with obesity and diabetes epidemics occurring in both adults and children.

Eating, in our culture, is closely connected with feeling good, which is heavily promoted in the media with images of extravagantly enormous meals, eating in high-end restaurants, exotic locations, and, of course, those full-out, holiday food spreads. I sometimes think that eating is the last, uncomplicated pleasure we humans have—that is, if you equate eating whatever you want in whatever quantities you desire with having fun. If you know better, and you see the results of overeating and poor food choices on your quality of life, it's not so fun anymore.

In my first book, I mentioned several studies demonstrating that a reduced intake of calories— "caloric restriction"—improves health, slows the aging process, and increases lifespan in a wide variety of species from yeasts, nematodes, fruit flies, fish, rodents, dogs and, of course, to people.

By reduced calories, I mean a modest reduction, not a crash diet. If you're currently taking in 2,500 calories a day and you make a modest 10% reduction in that intake to 2,250 calories a day, you'll see and feel the difference. Inflammation (and maybe even your weight) will be reduced, your health will improve, and your life will be extended. That's a pretty good deal, but our personal history and even our culture has trained us to feel deprived if we don't get to eat anything and everything we want.

The sense of feeling deprived in relation to food is an example of an unquestioned, habitual, established belief which along with our other worldviews restricts our health and longevity.

Scientific evidence suggests that living organisms use energy from sources other than those described by biochemistry. In the late 1970s, Dr. Paul Webb studied human energy balances in his laboratory in Ohio. The results were surprising, especially in subjects who were overeating or undereating. He looked at data compiled by Wilbur Olin Atwater (1844 -1907) during his studies on human nutrition and metabolism. Atwater, a chemist, is credited with laying the groundwork for the science of nutrition in the United States. While at Wesleyan University, Atwater, along with fellow Wesleyan scientist, Francis Gano Benedict, invented and used the respiration calorimeter to precisely measure the energy provided by food. These researchers created a system to measure this energy in units—known as food calories—in what became known as the Atwater system. This system comprised a four-foot by eight-foot chamber that housed a machine to measure human oxygen intake and carbon dioxide output. [24]

The experiments revealed serious discrepancies in seemingly available energy when test subjects were placed in conditions of vigorous exercise or were undereating. Atwater and Benedict arrived at their results by averaging data in situations where too much or too little energy was consumed. After Webb found more puzzling discrepancies in other studies, he concluded, "The more careful the study, the more clearly there is evidence of energy not accounted for." [25]

In his experiments, Webb kept a detailed log for three weeks on each of his subjects. He recorded changes in body weight, heat, and other forms of energy output, and measured how quickly subjects consumed oxygen and produced carbon dioxide. He found that more energy was being used than there were sources of this energy that he could explain. To address this mystery, Webb suggested there was an as-yet unrecognized and unmeasured kind of energy, which he called x. Amassing the data from all his studies, on average x represented 27 percent of the total metabolic expenditure. This means over a quarter of energy was unaccounted for by food intake. [25]

There have been accounts over the centuries of people who apparently live for months or even years without eating. The stories challenge everything we know about the physiology of the body, not to mention common sense. In India, the usual explanation for an individual's ability to live without food is the energy derived from sunlight or from the breath – in particular from *prana*, the life force within the breath. "Breatharians" are people who claim they are living with no food or small amounts of food. Sheldrake points out that the *prana* theory doesn't, in itself, defy the principle of the conservation of energy. Rather, it suggests that some people obtain their energy from a non-food source. [26]

To test if such a thing was possible, in 2010, a research team from the Indian Defence Institute of Physiology and Allied Sciences (DIPAS) investigated an 83-year-old yogi called Prahlad Jani, known as Mataji, who lived in the temple town of Anbaji in Gujarat. Mataji claims he hasn't eaten since 1940 and that the Hindu goddess Amba provides him a liquid sustenance or water that drops down through a hole in his palate, which allows him to live without food or drink. [26]

For the two-week duration of the DIPAS study, Mataji stayed in a hospital under constant observation, and he was videotaped on closed-circuit cameras. The yogi gargled on several occasions, but the medical team confirmed that he ate and drank nothing and passed no urine or feces over the two-week period. Another investigation in 2003 had similar results. The director of DIPAS said, "If a person starts fasting, there will be some changes in his metabolism, but in his [Jani's] case, we did not find any." This is note-worthy, because most people are able to survive a two-week fast. However, most of us would experience physiological changes that could be easily observed. [27]

The best-documented example in the 20th century of surviving for extended periods without food is that of the Bavarian mystic Therese Neumann (1898–1962). In 1918, Therese became partially paralyzed after falling off a stool in her uncle's barn. She continued to have episodes of falling and sustained injuries, culminating in her becoming totally blind and bedridden in 1919. In 1923, she refused all food and drink (except the Eucharist) and never ate again for the nearly 40 years until her death. Every Friday, she had visions of the passion of Christ and, like some other Roman Catholic mystics, bled profusely from wounds on her hands and feet, known as stigmata. [28]

Her decades-long fast and her stigmata drew public attention. In July of 1927, the Bishop of Regensburg appointed a commission, headed by physician, Otto Seidl, with the assistance of four Franciscan nurses, to study Neumann. She was physically examined and tested for fifteen days (July 14 - 28). Neumann was never observed to eat anything. At the beginning of this period, she weighed 121 pounds, and this dropped during the test period to 112.5 pounds. However, by the end of the 15 days, her weight had returned to normal. [27]

These accounts indicate that the energy available to living organisms may not solely depend on the caloric content of food and the physiology of metabolism. All organisms are linked to the larger flow of energy throughout Nature, which affects our conscious and subconscious minds as well as our physical selves.

Mostly, our energy levels don't have to do with our surroundings, however. We're the greatest source of our energy or lack thereof. The most obvious source of energy is food, but the kind of foods we eat, and the efficiency of our metabolism are important. Not all calories are created equal, and certainly the quality of our food—whether it's fresh and organic or processed and full of pesticides—makes a significant difference in the quality and quantity of the energy our body produces.

Another factor in our energy level is the biochemistry of our brain. Depressed people—who are lacking in the neurotransmitter serotonin, the "feel good" hormone—often feel exhausted. It could be argued that they feel physically tired not because their bodies are weak but because they're lacking in inspiring brain chemicals. In the same way, if we feel threatened, epinephrine (also known as adrenalin), the "fight-or-flight" neurotransmitter, kicks in, and we can often move faster than we'd ever believe possible. Epinephrine increases blood flow to muscles, causes our heart to beat faster to pump out more oxygen-rich blood, and elevates blood sugar, all of which give us a burst of energy.

Have you heard of "seasonal affective disorder" or SAD? This is a form of depression that affects 25 million Americans—mostly women—in the winter months. There's been much research done on this condition, and what seems to happen is the shortened hours of daylight during the winter cause lower levels of serotonin in the brain.

Along with depression, symptoms of SAD may include frequent napping, feelings of low self-esteem, becoming obsessed with details, irritability, and panic attacks. People with SAD often have poor sleep quality, even though they may be in bed for many hours, partly because they don't have enough serotonin to convert to the sleep-inducing hormone melatonin. Lastly, low levels of serotonin create a craving for sweets and simple carbs.

Other sources of energy are sunlight, air, and the earth. We know that vitamin D is essential for our health and wellbeing, and it only makes sense that energy we absorb from the sun through our skin energizes our bodies as well as affecting our mood and outlook. Studies have shown that vitamin D enhances our immune system, and we receive that powerful benefit if we expose our skin to sunlight for only a few minutes a day.

Air and earth are vitally important as well. Fresh air rejuvenates our energy, and putting our bare feet on the earth connects us with an enormous electromagnetic field created by the earth's rapid rotation while basking in the energy of the sun. All you need to do is stand facing the rising sun in the open air with your bare feet on the ground to feel the power you receive from all three of these energy sources.

And even gravity—which most of us are unaware of or have a bad opinion about because it seems to make it more difficult for us to move around—is essential for our strength and well-being. Studies of astronauts returning after prolonged periods in space have shown loss of bone density, and, in many other ways, weightlessness isn't good for the body. It affects the ability of certain immune cells to function and causes red blood cells to explode. It weakens all the muscles in the body, including the heart, because it doesn't provide the resistance we experience living with gravity which builds our strength.

Questions:

- Do you believe the energy to sustain your life comes solely from the food you eat?

- Have you ever experimented with reducing your food intake? Initially, did you have an internal voice that said you were starving?

In the course of this chapter, I have questioned some of the fundamental scientific beliefs that form our worldview today. It is not a vision of undeniable, objective truth rather it is a questionable belief system which has a profound effect on our health and the health of the planet.

As we have seen, facts and values are not clearly separated. Each of the five beliefs has aspects of myth, and ideology, and truth, on which they are based and have become unconscious habits of thought. With the suggested questions I introduce an initial level of dialogue that will be further developed in later chapters which questions our fundamental beliefs, and recognizes the plurality of sciences, natures, and points of view.

Let's move from examining global beliefs to looking at personal beliefs and stories that may be affecting our health and longevity.

References:

1. Sheldrake, Rupert. *Science Set Free: 10 Paths to New Discovery*; pp. 6-7. Potter/TenSpeed/Harmony. Kindle Edition
2. Ibid., p. 46
3. Classical physics. (2018, February 1). In *Wikipedia*. Retrieved from https://en.wikipedia.org/w/index.php?title=Classical_physics&oldid=823399357
4. Stapp HP. (2004) Mind, Matter, and Quantum Mechanics. In: Mind, Matter and Quantum Mechanics. The Frontiers Collection. Springer, Berlin, Heidelberg (pg. 234)
5. Schwartz, JM, Stapp, HP, Beauregard, M. Quantum physics in neuroscience and psychology: a neurophysical model of mind-brain interaction. *Phil Trans R Soc B.* doi:10.1098/rstb.2004.1598.
6. Ho, Mae-Wan. *The Rainbow and the Worm: The Physics of Organisms*; p. 269. World Scientific Publishing. Kindle Edition.
7. Sheldrake, Rupert. Ibid., p. 168.
8. James, W. (1950). *The Principles of Psychology*, 2 volumes in 1. New York: Dover Publications.
9. Sheldrake, Rupert, ibid., pp. 163-164.
10. Lipton, Bruce H. The Biology of Belief 10th Anniversary Edition: Unleashing the Power of Consciousness, Matter & Miracles; p. 27. Hay House, Inc. Kindle Edition.
11. Sheldrake, Rupert. Ibid., p. 165-169.
12. Rosenblum, Bruce. *Quantum Physics of Consciousness* (Kindle Locations 4027-4031). Cosmology Science Publishers. Kindle Edition.
13. Lipton, Bruce H. Ibid., p. 26-27. The Biology of Belief 10th Anniversary Edition: Unleashing the Power of Consciousness, Matter & Miracles; p. 27. Hay House, Inc. Kindle Edition.

14. Ibid., p. 27.
15. Nijhout, H. F. (1990), Problems and Paradigms: Metaphors and the role of genes in development. Bioessays, 12: 441–446. doi:10.1002/bies.950120908
16. Sheldrake, Rupert. Ibid. p. 187-188.
17. Ibid., p. 188-189.
18. Ibid., p. 198.
19. 119. Sheldrake, Rupert. Science Set Free: 10 Paths to New Discovery (p. 194). Potter/TenSpeed/Harmony. Kindle Edition.
20. Action at a distance. (2018, January 28). In *Wikipedia*. Retrieved from https://en.wikipedia.org/w/index.php?title=Action_at_a_distance&oldid=822820241
21. Lorenz, E.N., 1963: Deterministic Nonperiodic Flow. *J. Atmos. Sci.,* **20**, 130–141, https://doi.org/10.1175/1520-0469(1963)020<0130:DNF>2.0.CO;2
22. Brain Facts: A Primer on the Brain and Nervous System. (2012). Society of Neuroscience. Retrieved from https://www.unibs.it/sites/default/files/ricerca/allegati/Brain%20Facts_A%20primer.pdf
23. Lipton, Bruce H. Ibid. p. 132
24. Sheldrake, Rupert. Ibid. p. 76-77.
25. Ibid. p. 78.
26. Sheldrake, Rupert. Ibid., p. 79-80.
27. Rajeev Khanna (25 November 2003). "Fasting fakir flummoxes physicians." BBC News. Retrieved 2008-06-07.
28. Wilson, Ian. *The Bleeding Mind: An Investigation into the Mysterious Phenomena of Stigmata*. Weidenfeld and Nicholson. (1988); pp. 114-115. ISBN 0-297-79099-4.

Chapter 3
Biology and Beliefs

---

*"I seem to have been only like a boy
playing on the seashore, and diverting
myself in now and then finding a
smoother pebble or a prettier shell than
ordinary, whilst the great ocean of truth
lay all undiscovered before me."*

- Isaac Newton

Everyone is a collection of traits programmed by the genes inherited from his or her parents. This is our genetic makeup. It's what we begin with, but it doesn't define who we are.

In the 1980s, it was believed that, once the human genome was sequenced, we'd be able to predict and manipulate everything having to do with our physical selves. This didn't turn out to be the case, for several reasons. Essentially, it was determined that genes only code for protein expression and aren't a blueprint for how the body functions.

A good way to think of ourselves is that we're a collection of processes that are constantly changing. We're different from one moment to the next. This isn't an exaggeration. Our bodies and our thoughts are in a state of flux from the moment we're born. We can influence some of these changes—not all, but a lot—by what we eat, what we do, and what we think. However, even more important to our well-being and health than these conscious choices and attitudes is the power of our subconscious.

Consciousness, as we learned in Chapter 2, refers not only to the activities in our mind of which we're aware but also the activities of our subconscious mind as well. It's been determined that 80% of what influences our physical and mental functioning derives from the subconscious mind. [1]

In our subconscious mind reside our well-worn, habituated responses. In the context of energy and consciousness, these habituated responses restrict our lives by limiting our creativity and energy. In addition, they also affect our health and longevity. But these responses only retain their power if we remain unaware of them. Once we become mindful of our automatic reactions and behaviors—which are born of deep-seated emotions—we can begin to work with them and, eventually, control them. In this way, we can transform not only our reactions and behaviors but our health.

You're More Than Your DNA

Over the past several centuries, much has been learned about physiology, psychology, and medicine—the role of bacteria, viruses, nutrition, and stress as well as emotional trauma on our physical and mental health. In the last hundred years, much has been revealed about the role of genetics in everything from our appearance to our predisposition to disease. It seemed, for a while, that genetics would explain everything, and with this information, we could gain the upper hand on inherited disorders and tendencies. This has yet to happen.

In a lecture series that began in the 1950s, Sir Francis Crick articulated what became known as the "Central Dogma of Molecular Biology," which was formalized in an article which appeared in the journal *Nature* in 1970. [2] His thesis states that all information necessary for the processes of life is found in the DNA, with DNA as the only blueprint for both a cell's structure and function. Crick argued that information is transcribed from DNA via RNA (ribonucleic acid) to proteins, but information can't flow the opposite direction. In addition, according to the central dogma of molecular biology, no outside influence affects gene expression. [3] In other words, Crick proposed that genes determine the character of an organism because they control the synthesis of proteins.

For nearly 50 years, the central dogma of molecular biology was the accepted biological model. In 1994, Crick extended this model of genetic determinism to other aspects of human life, including emotional, behavioral, and mental processes, in his book, *The Astonishing Hypothesis: The Scientific Search for Soul.* [4] He stated in this book, "You, your joys and your sorrows, your memories and ambitions, your sense of personal identity and free will, are in fact nothing more than the behavior of a vast assembly of nerve cells and their associated molecules."

An understanding of genetics did, indeed, vastly expand our knowledge of how inherited traits affect our health and longevity. However, there are many other factors involved. We see this every day in our own lives, even in our own family. Our siblings have the same genes we have—though not in the same proportions, unless they're our twin—yet, one sibling experiences illness throughout his or her life and may even pass at a young age, while another has excellent health and lives a long time.

In 2011, nearly a decade after mapping the human genome, an article appeared in the *New England Journal of Medicine* that reported very little correlation between obesity, diabetes, and genes. [5] Type 2 diabetes and obesity are worldwide epidemics that many believed would be brought under control once we had a blueprint of the human genome.

More importantly, it's been shown that the chemistry of a cell isn't determined by its genes but by the cell's interaction with its environment. The biochemistry of cells is controlled by genes, but genes are influenced by the reactions of the cell to signals received from the environment.

Internal and external factors—what we think, how we react to stress, our degree of isolation or engagement, our diet, the toxins in our environment, our level of physical and mental activity, and our beliefs (in particular, our spiritual beliefs)—have as much to do with our health as does our DNA. These factors can turn genes on and off, which, in turn, control which proteins are expressed. These expressed proteins are what determine disease or health. This sequence of events triggered by internal and external influences that affect our genes can be defined in one word: epigenetics. [6]

The Role of Epigenetics in Our Health and Longevity

"Epi" is a Greek prefix that means "over, outside of, or around." Epigenetics refers to influences on our genetics—something additional to the genetic basis of inheritance. Wikipedia defines epigenetics as "stable heritable traits (phenotypes) that can't be explained by changes in the DNA sequence," a definition formulated at a meeting of geneticists held in Cold Spring Harbor Laboratory in December 2008. [7] Epigenetic effects on cellular and physiological heritable traits are often the result of external and environment factors, although they can be part of normal development. The definition of epigenetics requires these changes to be heritable, either in the progeny of cells or in organisms.

As discussed in Chapter 2, DNA has been considered to be the complete blueprint for living things, and this central hypothesis has been held by biologists for decades. More evidence is accumulating that all organisms acquire characteristics by interacting with their environment. Whether it is bacteria or a mammal, the environment affects characteristics, and these new characteristics can be passed to their offspring. This process is called "epigenetic inheritance." [8]

The take-home message of the last 15 years of research on human genetics is that our health—physical and mental—isn't prescribed by our DNA. Genes require instructions on what to do as well as when and where to do it. Each cell in our bodies contains the DNA to become any type of cell and perform any function—a heart cell has the same DNA as a brain cell—but a heart cell knows to only code for proteins needed for it to function as part of the heart. These code instructions are found not *in* the DNA but *on* it—in the form of chemical markers and switches. This is referred to as the epigenome. The markers and switches lie along the entire length of the DNA, so they are able to turn expression for genes on or off. The epigenome could be compared to a software program that induces the DNA to produce the necessary proteins and cell types. [9]

It's only been since the early 2000s that the epigenetic model of gene expression has been elucidated. Methylation and acetylation of genes are the primary mechanisms of action in this process. In methylation, methyl groups or clusters attach to the cytosine molecule of a DNA strand, which makes it more difficult to transcribe DNA, so gene expression is inhibited. In acetylation, acetyl groups promote gene expression by facilitating the unwrapping of the histone strands around which DNA is coiled, so the DNA is more easily able to be transcribed.

Here's a quick example of what this means: A study appeared in 2006 in which a gene called the Agouti gene was suppressed ("silenced") in laboratory mice. When the mother mouse ate a diet rich in methyl, the Agouti gene was silenced, and significant physiological effects were seen in her offspring. Mice with the silenced gene had half the incidence of cancer and diabetes and lived about twice as long as the non-methylated mice— indisputable evidence that the epigenome can affect health. [10]

Most startling, however, is the effect of emotions—in particular, nurturing—on the promotion on stress-reducing genes. In a study on rats published in 2005, researchers demonstrated that nurturing mothers, who groomed their offspring, had rats who grew up to better handle stress as adults. The nurtured rats had acetylation of genes in the regions of their brain responsible for regulating stress. The most remarkable observation was that not only did the mother's behavior produce this effect, but the behavior and resulting epigenomic modification were discovered to be heritable. Nurtured rat pups nurtured their own offspring in the same way, and their offspring had similar molecular changes *without any difference in the genetic sequence.* [11]

The Heritability of Epigenomes

When a gene undergoes a change as a result of an environmental factor—be it nurturing or an environmental toxin—that "epigenome" is passed down through the generations. This means that if one of your ancestors drank or smoked excessively or lived in an environmentally polluted place and these factors damaged that person's DNA, you may have that ancestor's damaged DNA in your cells.

We've known for a while that environmental effects like radiation can alter genetic sequences, and if this happens in a sex cell's DNA, these changes are carried forward through subsequent generations. We also know that what a pregnant mother ingests—be it good or bad—can alter the development of the fetus. What's new is the realization that the environment can change the epigenome and these alterations are heritable, without a single change in the genetic sequence. Now we know that what we eat, our behavior, and our emotional environment can affect not only our own health and that of our children but that of many generations to come. [12]

The belief that an individual's epigenome is established during fetal development has only recently been dispelled. Believe it or not, eating a certain food or receiving a dose of love can alter the software that influences our genes to create changes in our body and brain. Epidemiology and animal model studies suggest that nutrition during pregnancy not only affects the fetus but also future offspring as well. This is because when the epigenome is disrupted, there can be effects in future generations.

Recently, a group of researchers has been investigating not only the health of the mother but also the health of the father before conception and how his health influences the offspring's health. The possible impact of the reprogramming of methylation profiles on imprinted genes of the parents before conception, such as during spermatogenesis (sperm formation) or oogenesis (egg formation) was considered only a few years ago. The aim in this study was to determine associations between preconceptional obesity and DNA methylation profiles in the offspring, particularly at the differentially methylated regions (DMRs) of the imprinted Insulin-like Growth Factor 2 (IGF2) gene. [13]

The researchers concluded: "While our small sample size is limited, our data indicates a preconceptional impact of paternal obesity on the reprogramming of imprint marks during spermatogenesis. Given the biological importance of imprinting fidelity, our study provides evidence for transgenerational effects of paternal obesity that may influence the offspring's future health status."

Also in 2015, researchers in Denmark discovered that if a man is obese at the time he fathers a child, this can affect his sperm, which, in turn, affects his offspring. [14] This is different than the usual thinking about heredity—that genes coding for obesity, stress, or cancer are the sole influences on the offspring, whether or not the parent actually was obese or developed cancer.

In 2010, Dr. Romain Barres and colleagues at the University of Copenhagen did a simple experiment in which male rats were fed a high-fat diet (which made them obese) and then were mated with normal-weight female rats. Compared with male rats of normal weight, the animals on a high-fat diet fathered offspring that had a greater tendency to gain weight, become overweight, and had trouble regulating insulin levels. [15].

In another study, Barres and coworkers collected sperm from 10 obese Danish men and 13 men of normal weight. Numerous epigenetic differences were found in the sperm of the two groups. A significant difference was seen in the methylation status of the two cohorts—the methylation pattern differed in more than 9,000 genes between the lean and obese men.

Barres and colleagues then followed six obese men from the time they received bariatric surgery to see how losing weight changed these methylation patterns. A year after the surgery, over 3,900 genes were found to be methylated differently. Interestingly, some of the epigenetically altered genes are linked to appetite control. [16].

As interesting as these findings are, they don't prove that these alterations are passed down to the children of these men. Barres is now involved in work to compare epigenetic patterns in the sperm of obese fathers with the epigenetic patterns found in their offspring's blood cells to see what patterns are being transmitted. [17]

The Categories of Epigenomes

Epigenomes are often subdivided into categories based on the source of the factor causing the genetic mutation: the exposome, the nutrigenome, and the microbiome.

The Exposome

The exposome, as the name suggests, refers to environmental influences (both external and those within the body) on our genes that have health consequences. An article appearing in the October 2010 issue of *Science* magazine purports that 70% to 90% of an individual's risk of a particular disease is related to environmental exposure and its effects on the molecules in our bodies. The world of exposomes includes toxins, food, microbes, and chemicals within the body including all the biologically active molecules that control inflammation, oxidative stress, the balance of flora in the gut, and other natural processes. [18]

Technologies and diagnostics are being developed that will help us discover the environmental factors to which we've been exposed and allow us to remove at least some of them—mercury and pesticides, for example—from our environment. We can alter our internal environment as well by eating healthy organic food and taking probiotic supplements to assure our gut flora is balanced and therefore functioning at its best. Research over the last 10 years has shown how vitally important the flora in our gut is to our overall health. The gut has been described as "the body's second immune system," and some believe it's more important than our blood-based immune system in enhancing our resistance to disease.

The Nutrigenome

From the moment we're born, eating is our means of providing energy and building materials for our bodies, and, like the slogan says, "We are what we eat." Nutritionists divide the types of calories we consume into three categories—protein, fat, and carbohydrate—each of which is referred to as a macronutrient. Another component of our diet is micronutrients—vitamins and minerals. Fiber, phytonutrients (plant-based bioactive compounds), and all sorts of other components in our food have the ability to enhance or decrease signaling from our genes. This science of how what we eat affects the function of our genes is called nutrigenomics.

The Reality We Create

Michelle Grayson, former Assistant Editor of the journal *Nature*, made these comments in an essay that appeared in the December 2010 issue:

"Food affects people differently. Current nutritional research involves looking beyond ingredients in an attempt to understand the effects of food at genetic and epigenetic levels. From the first milk meal we take, through feast and famine; our genes influence our diet, and nutrients — or lack of them — affect gene expression.

Regional differences in food and culture have left their mark on our genome. Around the world, populations have adapted to their diet to make the most of local resources. In some instances, a foodstuff can protect against deadly infection, giving selective advantage to those who can readily digest it.

Nutrition has also directed the evolution of our species. Only *Homo sapiens* and our extinct hominin cousins have used fire to manipulate raw food, thereby creating safer, easily digestible and tastier recipes. Combined with the use of tools and an omnivorous, wide-ranging appetite, the advent of cooking increased the energy yield for metabolism and fed our enlarging brains.

Because food is packed full of complex, biologically active molecules, the fact it has an impact on our health is no surprise. Yet teasing apart the effects of each component on the body is a tall task, and one that will continue for many years to come. Some people predict an age of diets customized to individual energy needs and disease susceptibility.

Much has been made lately of diets based on our genetic make-up, both in terms of individuals and as a species. There's the blood-type diet that advocates consuming certain macronutrients (or proportions of them) based on whether your blood type is O, A, B, or AB. There's the paleo diet which argues that our distant ancestors ate mostly meat and plants, so that's what we should be doing to create optimum health. We may argue the merits of these various diets, but one thing is clear—what we eat changes gene expression in our bodies, and does so in a timeframe of as little as weeks. In 2008, Dr. Dean Ornish published a now-famous study demonstrating the beneficial effects of eating a plant-based, whole-foods diet on more than 500 cancer-controlling genes in patients with prostate cancer. [19]

The Microbiome

One of the most influential actors in our bodies—the mitochondria—was originally a bacterium that migrated into the nucleus of human cells to become an essential part of our energy-producing machinery. If that's not weird enough, consider that there are some 100 trillion microorganisms living inside our bodies. The DNA of these microorganisms outnumbers our own DNA a hundred-fold. The entirety of this population of microorganisms is called the microbiome.

The gut flora we mentioned above is a subpopulation of this microbiome. There are about 500 different kinds of bugs living in your intestines—and this is mostly a good thing. However, imbalance in the microbiome has been linked to a wide variety of health conditions from allergies to autoimmune disorders to cancer to cardiovascular disease to metabolic disorders and obesity. In addition, the overuse—and misuse—of antibiotics over the last seventy years, both in humans and in the food animals we grow and consume, has altered the populations of bacteria residing in our gut.

It basically comes down to this: The types and ratios of flora in our intestines have a strong influence on whether we'll be lean or overweight, healthy or suffering from chronic inflammation. The addition of pre- and probiotics to our diet is a simple way to restore a healthy gut ecosystem.

Now that we've talked about some of the powerful hidden physical and physiological influences on our genes and our health, we're going to talk about an even deeper layer of influences—those in our psyche.

How Early Trauma, Stress, Thought Patterns, and Beliefs Affect Our Health

Telomeres are considered the most reliable aging marker. What are they? Telomeres are the base pairs at the ends of our DNA strands, and our lifestyle can increase or decrease telomerase activity. For example, stressful prenatal developmental experiences, childhood abuse (both verbal and physical), domestic violence, post-traumatic stress, nutritional deficiencies, and lack of love all inhibit telomerase activity. All of these factors are associated with poor health and a shorter lifespan. There are lifestyle factors that can improve telomerase activity, too. Exercise, good nutrition, a positive attitude, living in happiness and gratitude, being in service, and experiencing love—especially love of oneself—all stimulate telomerase activity. In doing so, these behaviors promote a longer, healthier life. [20]

Comparative studies of the health of identical twins raised in the same environment are enlightening in this regard. In one study, the cellular ages of identical twins in their late thirties were determined by telomere assay. One of these individuals had led a relatively stress-free life and the other a stressful life. One sister had a husband with Huntington's disease, which caused him to act violently and abusively toward those around him. She cared for her husband for years and experienced high levels of emotional stress, before his passing. Her cellular age, based on telomeric evaluation, was 10 years older than that of her genetically identical sibling. [20]

The Profound Effects of Adverse Childhood Experiences (ACEs) on Our Health and Our Longevity

A landmark longitudinal epidemiological study, the Adverse Childhood Experience (ACE) study, cosponsored by the Centers for Disease Control (CDC) and Kaiser Permanente, examined the relationship between childhood stress and adult disease in 17,337 adults. Not surprisingly, this study found there were higher rates of cancer, cardiovascular disease, diabetes, hypertension, and many other illnesses in adults who'd experienced adverse events as children. The median age of the people sampled in this study was 57 years. [21]

Let's look more closely at ACEs, because they have probably more impact on us than most things in our lives. For the purposes of the CDC-Kaiser Permanente study, ACEs were categorized into three groups: abuse, family/household challenges, and neglect. Each category was divided into more specific subcategories. Everyone had an ACE score of 0 to 10. Each type of trauma counted as one in this scoring system, no matter how many times that type of event occurs. Participant demographic information was provided by gender, race, age, and education. The categories and prevalence of ACEs by gender can be seen in the following table.

Table 1. Prevalence of ACEs by Category for CDC-Kaiser ACE Study Participants by Gender

ACE Category	Women Percent (N = 9,367)	Men Percent (N = 7,970)	Total Percent (N = 17,337)
ABUSE			
Emotional abuse	13.1%	7.6%	10.6%

Physical abuse	27%	29.9%	28.3%
Sexual abuse	24.7%	16%	20.7%
HOUSEHOLD CHALLENGES			
Mother treated violently	13.7%	11.5%	12.7%
Household substance abuse	29.5%	23.8%	26.9%
Household mental illness	23.3%	14.8%	19.4%
Parental separation or divorce	24.5%	21.8%	23.3%
Incarcerated household member	5.2%	4.1%	4.7%
NEGLECT			
Emotional neglect	16.7%	12.4%	14.8%
Physical neglect	9.2%	10.7%	9.9%

Source: Centers for Disease Control and Prevention, Kaiser Permanente. The ACE Study Survey Data [Unpublished Data]. Atlanta, Georgia: U.S. Department of Health and Human Services, Centers for Disease Control and Prevention; 2016.

The following table indicates the percentage of men and women based on the number of different categories of ACEs they experienced.

Table 2. ACE Score Prevalence for CDC-Kaiser ACE Study Participants by Gender

Number of Adverse Childhood Experiences (ACE Score)	Women Percent (N = 9,367)	Men Percent (N = 7,970)	Total Percent (N = 17,337)
0	34.5%	38.0%	36.1%
1	24.5%	27.9%	26.0%
2	15.5%	16.4%	15.9%
3	10.3%	8.5%	9.5%
4 or more	15.2%	9.2%	12.5%

Source: Centers for Disease Control and Prevention, Kaiser Permanente. The ACE Study Survey Data [Unpublished Data]. Atlanta, Georgia: U.S. Department of Health and Human Services, Centers for Disease Control and Prevention; 2016.

We can summarize the key takeaways from this study as follows:

- ACEs are common—nearly two-thirds (64%) of adults have had at least one.
- ACEs increase risk of adult onset of chronic disease, such as cancer and heart disease, as well as mental illness, violence, and being a victim of violence.
- ACEs rarely occur singly—if a person has one, there's an 87% chance that individual will have two or more.

- With each ACE, a person's risk for chronic disease, mental illness, violent behavior, and being a victim of violence increases.
- ACEs are responsible for a significant portion of workplace absenteeism and for healthcare, emergency response, mental health, and criminal justice costs.
- In summary, childhood adversity contributes to most of our major chronic health, mental health, economic health, and social health issues. [22]

Here are some more statistics drawn from this study: People with an ACE score of 4 are twice as likely to be smokers and seven times more likely to be alcoholic. Having an ACE score of 4 increases the risk of emphysema or chronic bronchitis by nearly 400 percent and suicide by 1200 percent. People with high ACE scores are more likely to be violent, to have more marriages, more broken bones, more drug prescriptions, more depression, and more autoimmune diseases. People with an ACE score of 6 or higher are at risk of their lifespan being shortened by 20 years. [22]

Clearly, what happens to us as children remains with us throughout our lives—not only in our memories but, perhaps even more extensively, in our bodies. Here's another example involving identical twins raised in the same environment. A study of six-year-old twins—one of whom developed leukemia at age two—found that the child who developed cancer had undergone a tonsillectomy—a physically and emotionally traumatic event—at six months of age. [23]

Trauma experienced as adults can be just as devastating as ACEs in terms of its effect on the development of illness. Studies of veterans who participated in the conflicts in Vietnam, Iraq, and Afghanistan and subsequently developed post-traumatic stress disorder (PTSD) after experiencing combat utilize medical services at a much higher rate than those veterans not suffering from PTSD. [24]

These are just a few examples demonstrating the relationship between physical and psychological distress and the development of disease. In short, emotional states are epigenetic—they regulate gene expression. In the same way, when stressful psychological states are relieved or the methods to deal with stress are improved, this results in beneficial changes in gene expression, which manifests as improved health and a longer life.

To learn about an effective therapy that addresses traumatic events in our life, see Appendix 3 on Brainspotting.

How Diet Can Change Your Epigenome

In 2000, Randy Jirtle, a professor of Radiation Oncology at Duke University, along with his postdoctoral student, Robert Waterland, were able to change the genetic expression in offspring of Agouti mice that carried a gene rendering them particularly susceptible to cancer and diabetes. These mice were always yellow in color and always obese as a result of one gene—the Agouti gene. When a male and female of this breed of mouse mated, all their offspring grew up to be fat, yellow, and ravenous. [25]

Jirtle and Waterland, however, bred an Agouti pair that produced lean, gray-brown mice *without altering the genes of the parents in any way.* These mice also didn't manifest their parents' susceptibility to cancer and diabetes. It seemed the Agouti gene wasn't being expressed—but why? The answer was simple, and groundbreaking—the Agouti mice that produced the normal offspring received a special diet.

Both Agouti parents were given a diet rich in certain so-called methyl donors. Methyl donors are necessary for methylation; methyl can attach to a particular gene and turn it off. These molecules are found particularly in certain vegetables—beets, garlic, onions—and in the food supplements that pregnant women often take. It was discovered that the Agouti gene passed, intact, to the offspring of the parents eating this diet but had been turned off. [25]

How What You Think Affects Your Epigenome

It doesn't take much reflection for us to realize that what we think, the beliefs we hold, and the emotions we feel are very fluid. Last week we were beside ourselves with worry about something, and today we can barely remember what that was. We're highly susceptible to changes in our emotions and thoughts. Scientists refer to the ability of our brain to be influenced by our thoughts and beliefs as plasticity—the brain's ability to establish and dissolve connections among its different parts.

How brain cells communicate with each other is complex to describe, so we won't go there, but what needs to be mentioned is that chemicals are involved in this communication process, and many of these chemicals (called neurotransmitters) have emotional signatures. Serotonin, for example, makes us feel happy. People who have insufficient serotonin bathing their brains typically feel depressed. Another chemical, oxytocin, which is released in the pituitary gland of women in labor, creates feelings of trust and attachment.

Every thought releases neuropeptides that trigger the release of certain kinds of hormones into the bloodstream to create a particular emotional experience. These chemicals not only affect how we feel but also create reactions everywhere in our body. We've all had the experience of being startled and then feeling the rush of adrenaline through our body in response. Every time we have a certain thought, or a certain memory comes to mind, a chemical is produced in our brain that creates reverberations in our body. Usually these effects are so subtle and fleeting that they're outside our conscious awareness.

64

However, sometimes we can think about something that happened years or even decades ago and experience our body's reaction to that memory.

Some thoughts are powerful enough to act as immune boosters, antidepressants, sedatives, stimulants, or other "drugs." Most of us have had the experience of listening to someone talk about an idea or experience they've had and feeling a strong urge to act on the idea or have the experience ourselves. Not only do we feel emotionally charged, our heart rate might increase, or we feel a sense of excitement or even urgency. In the same way, we can watch the news and have powerful emotions arise—anger, fear, hatred—because of thoughts generated by what we're seeing.

Psychoneuroimmunity (PNI) is the study of the effect of our thoughts on our immune system. PNI researchers have found that negative and stress-inducing thoughts depress our immunity and raise our T-cell count. T-cells are associated with inflammation, which is the body's response when it feels it's under attack.

Science has shown that our level of confidence affects our performance—but most of us don't need scientists to tell us that. We've all had the experience of feeling confident—whether it's prior to taking an exam or going out on a date—and how our sense of self-worth affects our outcomes.

Thoughts can arise from any of the five senses, although most are created as a result of the senses of sight and hearing. All thoughts are based on our unique perception of reality—not on reality itself, which none of us can ever know. As such, thoughts are colored by expectations and unconscious tendencies, which are habits of mind derived from an individual's beliefs, values, needs, psychological rules, self-concept, and emotions. These determine if our thoughts are positive or negative, which, in turn, largely determines if we're an optimistic, confident person or an individual struggling with self-doubt and low self-esteem.

How (and Why) We Hardwire Our Brain to Create Illness and Mental Suffering

The average human has some 60,000 thoughts a day, of which 95% are habitual thoughts—which means they arise in our mind every day or almost every day. These thoughts have a chronic effect on our body and our cells, and, by changing these thoughts, we can recreate our body and our cells.

So, why do many of us get stuck in the same, repetitive, negative "stories" about ourselves, even when we're aware this doesn't make us feel good? The reason is that our habitual thoughts and responses become hardwired in our brains if they're repeated enough times. You could envision it as a well-worn path which is easy to travel down.

Our brain is comprised of millions of neurons (nerve cells), which are composed of an axon, a nucleus, and dendrites. Whenever a thought arises in our brain, an electrical impulse travels between the synaptic gap (the space between two neurons). These transmissions create dendrite synaptic protuberances (DSPs) each time a mental event occurs—thinking, talking, feeling, or a decision to act. DSPs allow information to travel from one neuron to another. If we have repeated thoughts about the same thing, these thoughts are able to travel this pathway with increasingly less effort, and this is how habitual thoughts are formed. It's easier to travel a well-trodden pathway to create a new trail, so, out of laziness (or fear), we're reluctant to consider new ways of thinking. As a result, our thoughts and behaviors become hardwired.

In addition to the hardwiring, we can become addicted to the chemicals released by neurons when they fire. For example, dopamine is a major player in addictive behavior. The brain has multiple dopamine pathways, and one of these pathways is key in reward-motivated behavior. Most rewards will trigger a release of dopamine in the brain. Many addictive substances

66

also increase dopamine activity. Consider those sugar cravings you have, which are driven by the microbiome in your gut (bacteria in your gut wanting sugars to fuel growth). Once you have that doughnut, dopamine is released which sets up a positive feedback loop to reinforce that sugar craving.

However, dopamine isn't just released when we engage in addictive behavior. It's released any time we have a thought that makes us feel good. For example, consider how you feel once you have completed a project you have been working on for a while There is a sense of wellbeing (dopamine) and a feeling of relaxation as some of the pressure you were under is released.

If we take time to observe some of our thoughts and decisions, we can begin to identify some of the re-occurring patterns. Here are some patterns you may find familiar:

Overgeneralization – You take a single negative event as a statement of who you are. If your performance falls short of perfect, you see yourself as a total failure.

Mind reading – You arbitrarily conclude that someone is reacting negatively to you, and you don't bother to check this out.

Emotional Reasoning – You trust your emotions as the compass in your life. If you have a negative emotion you assume that reflects the way things really are: "I feel it, therefore it must be true."

Disqualifying the positive – Positive experiences don't count in your life for some reason. In this way you can maintain a negative belief that is contradicted by your everyday experiences.

Should Statements – You try to motivate yourself with shoulds and shouldn'ts, as if you had to be whipped and punished before you could be expected to do anything. "Musts" and "oughts" are also offenders. The emotional consequence is guilt. When you direct should statements toward others, you feel anger, frustration, and resentment.

The exercise of observing your thoughts is not to change anything or to judge yourself, rather it is to get a little below the surface of the thought pattern.

Habitual Thoughts Lead to Ingrained Patterns of Behavior

Our habitual thoughts lead to habitual ways of perceiving, interpreting, evaluating, feeling, and responding—all of which are learned (consciously or unconsciously) and practiced until we no longer notice them. Eventually, this thought-action pathway is so habituated that it becomes unconscious. Our lack of awareness about our patterns leads to mindless behavior— behavior in which our conscious mind is oblivious. We all know people (maybe we're one of them) who always see the worst possible outcome in any situation. Whatever it is, they immediately see how it will go bad and, usually, they express their opinion about it. That's habitual thinking which leads to a predictable pattern of response. Often this habituated response is not optimal for our emotional wellbeing, or our health. [26]

Stress Enhances Cognitive Aging—and Changes Your Epigenome

A study was published in 2015 that looked at the association of stress with cognitive aging, physiology, and emotion. This research, known as the ESCAPE study, noted that more than 5.4 million adults over the age of 70 have cognitive impairment (such as memory loss) without dementia and another 4.7 million have been diagnosed with Alzheimer's dementia. [26] Research suggests that psychological stress is an important risk factor in the development of cognitive impairment and dementia. Many aspects in our lives can't be controlled, but we *can* do something to reduce our stress.

We've all had the experience of having a stressful incident— even a very brief one, like a tense exchange over the phone— that has repercussions throughout the day. Our work isn't up to par or we forget things. People who experience chronic stress have even greater difficulty focusing and staying on track mentally, and this can lead to accelerated cognitive decline. Research cited in the ESCAPE study indicates that "minor daily stressors can produce transient effects on cognition by reducing the amount of attentional resources available for information processing." When we experience stress in our lives, we allocate our cognitive resources (our thinking) to trying to cope with the stress, and this, argue the researchers, lowers cognitive performance during non-stressful times. [27]

Chronic stress has also been implicated in short-term increases in inflammation as well as negative mood, both of which are associated with fatigue. Fatigue makes it more difficult to cope with stress, initiating a downward spiral of stress-inflammation-fatigue-increased stress. The ESCAPE study cited dozens of investigations that demonstrated a direct relationship between chronic life stress, cognitive decline, and increased incidence of dementia. [27]

One explanation for this connection is that chronic stress creates abnormal endocrine function and pro-inflammatory effects that can impair the neural structure and function that underlies cognitive function.

Tying this in with our previous discussion about habitual thinking, it's been hypothesized that repetitive thoughts— defined as thinking attentively, repetitively, or frequently about oneself or one's world—strongly contribute to the effects of stress on the body and mind.

The Good News—Your Thinking Can Change Your Epigenome, Improve Your Health, and Prolong Your Life

If we truly want to change our patterns, we need to pay attention to our thoughts. That is, we need to be mindful of our mind. We need to have the ability to stand back from our own thought processes and watch ourselves react. This is the only way we can change habitual responses as well as their corresponding behavior patterns.

When you remind yourself to look at your thoughts and notice what you're thinking—for example, making a judgment about someone—something magical happens. You watch yourself making a judgment, and you consciously create the thought, "I don't want to judge that person; I want to appreciate her." Just by having that thought, you achieve your goal, at least to a small degree.

Every time you catch yourself thinking negative thoughts—about yourself, another person, a situation—you have the opportunity to consider "changing your mind." You start creating a new pathway, and every time you walk down that pathway and realize how good it feels to stop your negative thinking, that pathway gets easier to travel.

Best of all, your life will change when your thoughts change. If you decide you want to be kind, you can make a point of substituting a kind thought every time you have an unkind thought, and amazingly (it seems), kindness becomes your mental environment. And—here's more (seeming) magic—you'll change your epigenome and become healthier.

A major study in 2008 demonstrated how simple behavioral interventions can affect gene expression. In one study, gene expression was compared among groups of people who practiced the stress-reduction method called the Relaxation Response with those who didn't use this method. The people who practiced this stress-reduction method had a very different gene expression than those who didn't use the method. [28]

The group that didn't engage in the Relaxation Response were then taught how to do it, and their gene expression was retested eight weeks later. The researchers found that the expression of 1,561 genes in these individuals had changed, including those responsible for free-radical scavenging, inflammation, and apoptosis (programmed cell death). The study tracked changes on the cellular level, but on the conscious level, practitioners of the Relaxation Response reported feelings of enhanced well-being, greater calmness and clarity, and a more optimistic outlook. [28]

In the next chapter, we'll investigate the nature of our reality—the quantum world.

References:

1. Science News Vol.115, No 2 (Jan.13 1979), p.23
2. Crick, F. Central dogma of molecular biology. *Nature.* 1970;227:561.
3. Church, D. (2010). Your DNA is Not Your Destiny: Behavioral Epigenetics and the Role of Emotions in Health. *Anti-Aging Medical Therapeutics*, 13.
4. Crick, F. *The Astonishing Hypothesis: The Scientific Search for Soul.* New York, NY: Scribner's, 1994.
5. McCarthy, M.I. 2010. Genomics, type 2 diabetes, and obesity. *N Engl J Med.* 363(24): 2339-50. Review.
6. Shaw, Jonathan, "Is Epigenetics Inherited." Harvard Magazine Web May-June 2017
7. Epigenetics. (2018, April 12). In Wikipedia. Retrieved from https://en.wikipedia.org/w/index.php?title=Epigentics&oldid=836044538.
8. Brodin, et al, Variation in the human immune system is largely driven by non-heritable influences, Cell. 2015 Jan 15;160(1-2):37-47. doi: 10.1016/j.cell.2014.12.020.
9. Handy DE, Castro R, Loscalzo J. Epigentic Modifications: Basic Mechanisms and Role in Cardiovascular Disease. Circulation. 2011;123(19):2145-2156. doi:10.1161/CIRCULATIONHA.110.956839.
10. Dolinoy DC, Weidman JR, Waterland RA, Jirtle RL. Maternal genistein alters coat color and protects Agouti mouse offspring from obesity by modifying the fetal epigenome. *Environ Health Perspect.* 2006;114:567-572.
11. Weaver IC, Champagne FA, Brown SE, Dymov S, Sharma S, Meaney MJ, Szyf M. Reversal of maternal programming of stress responses in adult offspring through methyl supplementation: altering epigenetic marking later in life. *J Neurosci.* 2005;25:11045-11054.

12. Watters, E. DNA Is Not Destiny: The New Science of Epigenetics. *Discover Magazine*, November 22, 2006.
13. Adelheid S, Schildkraut JM, Murtha A, Wang F, Huang Z, Bernal A, Kurtzberg J, Jirtle RL, Murphy SK and Hoyo C. Paternal obesity is associated with IGF2 hypomethylation in newborns: results from a Newborn Epigenetics Study (NEST) cohort. BMC Medicine. 2013; 11:29. https://doi.org/10.1186/1741-7015-11-29.
14. Donkin, I. et al. Obesity and Bariatric Surgery Drive Epigenetic Variation of Spermatozoa in Humans. Cell Metabolism 23, 369–378.
15. Sheau-Fang N, Lin RCY, Laybutt DR, Barres R, Owens JA, and Morris MJ. Chronic high-fat diet in fathers programs B-cell dysfunction in female rat offspring. Nature 467:963-966 (21 October 2010). Doi:10.1038/nature09491.
16. Donkin I, Versteyhe S, Ingerslev LR, Qian K, Mechta M, Nordkap L, Mortensen B, Appel EVR, Jørgensen N, Kristiansen VB, Hansen T, Workman CT, Zierath JR, and Barres R. Obesity and Bariatric Surgery Drive Epigenetic Variation of Spermatozoa in Humans. Cell Metabolism 23, 1-10. February 9, 2016.
17. Barse, Marie "Obesity can be passed on through the father's sperm." ScienceNordic Web, December 13, 2015]
18. Rappapport, S., et al. 2010. Environment and disease risks. Science. 330: 460-461.
19. Ornish, D., Magbanua, M.J., Weidner, G., et al. 2008. Changes in prostate gene expression in men undergoing an intensive nutrition and lifestyle intervention. Proc Natl Acad Sci USA. 105(24): 8369-74.
20. Fraga MF, Ballestar E, Paz MF, et al. Epigenetic differences arise during the lifetime of monozygotic twins. Proc Natl Acad Sci USA. 2005; 102:10604-10609.

21. Felitti JV, Anda RF, Nordenberg D, Williamson DF, Spitz AM, Edwards V, Koss MP, and Marks, JS. Relationship of childhood abuse and household dysfunction to many of the leading causes of death in adults. The Adverse Childhood Experience (ACE) Study. Am J Prev Med. 1998;14:245-258.

22. Centers for Disease Control and Prevention, Kaiser Permanente. The ACE Study Survey Data [Unpublished Data]. Atlanta, Georgia: U.S. Department of Health and Human Services, Centers for Disease Control and Prevention; 2016.

23. Church, D. (2010). Your DNA is Not Your Destiny: Behavioral Epigenetics and the Role of Emotions in Health. *Anti-Aging Medical Therapeutics*, 13.

24. Tanielian T, Jaycox LH, eds. *Invisible Wounds of War: Psychological and Cognitive Injuries, Their Consequences, and Services to Assist Recovery.* Santa Monica, CA: Rand Corp. 2008.

25. Watters, E. DNA Is Not Destiny: The New Science of Epigenetics. *Discovery Magazine*, November 22, 2006.

26. Burns, D. D. (1981). Feeling good: The new mood therapy. New York, N.Y: Penguin Books.

27. BMC Psychiatry. 2015. The Effects of Stress on Cognitive Aging, Physiology and Emotion (ESCAPE) Project. DOI: 10.1186/s12888-015-0497-7.

28. Dusek JA, Out HH, Wohlhueter AL, Bhasin M, Zerbini LF, Joseph MG, Benson H, and Libermann TA. Genomic counter-stress changes induced by the relaxation response. PLoS One. 2008;3:e2576.

Chapter 4
Our Quantum World

"Consciousness sleeps in minerals,
dreams in plants, wakes up in animals,
and becomes self-aware in humans"

- Rumi

In this chapter, we're going to explore how quantum theory has opened the door to a profoundly new vision of the world in which the observer, the observed, and the act of observation are fundamentally interlocked. As such, the very large, very small, very near, and very far are also interconnected.

Explicitly introducing the mind into the universe's functioning was the most radical shift in the understanding of quantum mechanics. The role of human experience changed from "a detached observer" to that of "the fundamental element of interest." [1]

In physics, a "quantum is defined as the smallest amount of a physical quantity that can exist independently, especially a discrete quantity of electromagnetic radiation or this amount of energy regarded as a unit." [2] The following overview of the quantum world isn't technical. My goal is to identify for you some of the key concepts of quantum theory that are discussed in upcoming chapters on quantum approaches to understanding the human body and mind and quantum theory as it relates to consciousness.

Our perception of reality evolves every time we edit "the program" (the current belief system) that describes this reality. In the previous chapters, we explored how our current beliefs shape our world view. This is also what happened in the case of classical physics, which was the de facto "reality" (a word that should always be armed with quote marks, because no absolute reality exists) for some four hundred years. Physicists discovered that some of the premises and explanations of classical physics were inaccurate or incomplete, and the program was updated accordingly. Changing a part of the program is crucial to changing reality itself, because each new reality carries more information—and often that new information dislodges our existing model of beliefs.

Characteristics of the Quantum World

One of the foundations in quantum physics is the understanding that every object in the universe has properties of both a particle and a wave. Light is usually thought of as a wave, but it's actually made of photons. Photons are discrete energy bundles, and although they are not visible, their existence has been verified through experiments. We normally think of electrons as particles, but they have a wave nature that has been directly observed, just like organic molecules and all other material objects. [3]

Another aspect of the quantum world is that everything is connected—even objects across the universe from one another. Everything in nature is fundamentally interconnected, beyond time and space. Information can be exchanged between any two objects instantaneously—no matter their space-time separation—and these interconnections can't be blocked or weakened.

Just these two attributes of quantum physics—the ability of an object to be both particle and wave and the interconnectedness of all things beyond the limits of time and space—give us a small indication of what we don't know about reality. We base our understanding of reality primarily on information derived from our senses and our logical mind. Of course, most of us have had intuitive experiences—hunches, nudges, or feelings for which there was seemingly no reasonable basis but which we just *knew* were true. Intuition provides only the smallest hint of how much our unconscious mind—our "dark" mind, if you will—influences us.

Anything that exists in this Universe, anything to which you think of as being "real", only exists based on the information it is sharing with other objects in the universe—i.e., everything is interconnected. Nothing else exists, nothing else has any underlying reality, and hence there's no infinite regression. It just has to be this way, because otherwise we're asking a finite universe to contain an infinite amount of information—and this is clearly not possible!

According to the principles of quantum mechanics, all matter—from the tiny subatomic particles to the largest objects in the cosmos and everything in between—displays the characteristics of entanglement, coherence, correlation, and resonance. [4] In addition, at the quantum level, entities appear completely differently than they do in our experience of the everyday world. It's more accurate to say there are no entities at the quantum level—there are only the *possibilities* for the experience of entity-ness, so to speak. [5]

If that isn't confusing enough, consider this: Many of the substances we identify as 'matter' can exist in various states: solid, liquid, and gas. The more energetic a form of matter becomes, the more distant the molecules comprising it travel from each other due their increased kinetic energy. When this happens, matter becomes less solid. We move quite freely through air—so much so that we often don't think of it as matter, but air is as much matter as concrete. Concrete, however, is much more 'congealed,' so to speak, because the molecules comprising it are moving less rapidly than the molecules of air and, as a result, are closer together. However, this doesn't alter the fact that all matter is actually 99.999999999999 percent empty space—yes, even concrete.

There's no solid, extended, continuous, and impenetrable 'stuff' that creates the appearance and qualities of solid materiality; rather, this appearance and quality are the result of the nuclear and electromagnetic forces that hold matter together. All this is a way of saying that what we perceive as reality in our physical world is completely misleading. And that, in a nutshell, is the take-home message from quantum physics.

However, as Aldous Huxley is quoted as saying, "The world is an illusion, but it is an illusion which we must take seriously, because it is real as far as it goes ..." [6]

The Quantum Approach

The quantum view of physics remedied many of the shortcomings of classical physics. Scientists felt the principles of classical physics were inadequate to describe the physical world and our role in it. Quantum theory was utilized to draw a connection between physical or mathematical properties and the human psychological experience.

Quantum approaches dismantled classical physics theories that focused on the world outside the human rather than a world that referenced human thoughts. "The core idea of quantum mechanics is to describe both *our activities as knowledge-seeking and knowledge-acquiring agents,* and *the knowledge that we thereby acquire."* [7] Quantum theory shifts humans from observers in a passive role to agents in an active role.

As such, the agent's conscious choices about how to act affects the physical system being acted upon, which, in turn influences the knowledge acquired from these systems. One reason why consciousness wasn't accessible to science is because it wasn't considered objective. In other words, the belief was that consciousness is the light the observer throws on objects, but this light can't be turned upon itself. Quantum theory changed all of that.

The origins of quantum theory emerged from the work of Niels Bohr when he was working at an institute in Copenhagen and is thus referred to as 'the Copenhagen interpretation.' "In the great drama of existence, we ourselves, are both actors and spectators." Quantum theory introduces the possibility of humans as actors rather than simply spectators.

Specifically, this relates to one of the central conundrums of quantum physics—the measurement problem. This has to do with the nature and significance of making a measurement within a quantum system. The conundrum derives from the fact that the outcome of a quantum experiment can change depending on whether the observer chooses to measure a particular property of the particles involved. This is often the result of instruments used to observe the phenomenon. For example, it isn't possible for the human eye to detect an object unless light is hitting that object and makes it visible. While the effects of observation are often negligible, the object viewed nonetheless experiences a change. [8]

This was known as the "observer effect" and caused some researchers to conclude that it isn't possible to be objective and that consciousness plays a necessary role in quantum theory. Physicists have discovered that even passive observation of quantum phenomena (that is, observations in which nothing is measured, nor the phenomenon acted on in any way) can change the phenomenon. The Weizmann experiment, conducted in 1998, is a famous example. This was a highly controlled experiment demonstrating how a beam of electrons is influenced by the act of being observed. With more "watching," the observer's influence had a greater effect on what actually took place. [9] These findings led to speculation that the conscious mind can actually affect reality, although not all physicists agree with this. [10]

The Reality We Create

The observer effect can be seen in many areas of physics, but it can often be reduced to an essentially insignificant effect with the use of different instruments and observation techniques. The so-called "double-slit experiment" brought the observer effect into sharp focus and profoundly changed the world as we know it. For this experiment, a beam of light is set up to shine through a screen with two, closely spaced, parallel slits. The light then passes through the slits and strikes another screen some distance away that's parallel to the screen with the slits. Considering the light that emerges from the slits is in the form of waves, when these waves of light emerge from the two slits, they interfere with each other, just as the ripples on the surface of a pond into which two stones have been thrown interfere with each other. If the peaks of the waves coincide, they reinforce each other. If a peak and a trough coincide, they cancel one another out. In light, this wave interference is called diffraction. In the double-slit experiment, this diffraction produces a series of alternating bright and dark stripes on the screen, representing where the light waves are either reinforced or cancelled out. [8]

If the double-slit experiment is performed with quantum particles—electrons, for example—these particles behave as waves. That is, they undergo diffraction after passing through the slits and produce an interference pattern just as the light waves did. However, if these electrons pass through the slits one by one, their arrival on the screen is seen one by one. Even though there's apparently nothing for each particle to interfere with on its journey, the pattern of these individual particles arriving at the screen creates, over time and with the arrival of billions of particles, the same light and dark bands of interference. This seems to suggest that each particle passes simultaneously through both slits and interferes with itself. This phenomenon of a single particle taking two paths at the same time is known as the superposition state. [8]

OK, this is all pretty strange—that one particle can be two places and pass through two slits at the same time—but wait, there's more. If a detector is placed inside or just behind one slit, it's possible to determine whether a given particle goes through that particular slit or not. When such a detector is put in place, the interference vanishes, meaning the bands disappear and what's left if a solid pattern. The detector—even though it doesn't interact with the particle in any way—changes the outcome simply by observing the behavior of the particle.

This brings us back to that statement about the *possibility* of quantum entities that we mentioned earlier. In the same way, the behavior of a quantum particle exists as a cloud of possibilities and, when we observe an individual particle, the mass of possibilities collapses into a single, well-defined state or behavior.

The observer—the person who designs and conducts the observation experiments—plays a key role in affecting the quantum world. Taking this to the next step, the notion of an observer implies the presence of consciousness. This leads to the hypothesis that it's consciousness that affects the behavior of quantum particles. Some experts in quantum mechanics go so far as to suggest that consciousness plays a critical role in the formation and evolution of the universe, even though many researchers in psychology and brain science regard consciousness as simply localized brain activity with no significance in the universe at large.

Quantum Terms

I'm including definitions of the terms below as a beginning practice for loosening up our thinking regarding what we believe about reality. Also, we'll discuss these phenomena in later chapters. Even if none of us is an expert on quantum physics, we can acknowledge that it proves to us we can't begin to fully understand the influences taking place in atoms, in our bodies, our minds, and our universe. However, we can accept that the manifestations of most of these influences are invisible to our senses and our reason.

Superposition state: Quantum superposition refers to the quantum theory that two, mutually exclusive events can coexist. As we discussed above, a well-known example is that light can behave both as a particle and as a wave. As mentioned previously, light, which we normally think of as a wave, comes in discrete bundles of energy called photons. Electrons, which we normally think of as particles, have a wave nature we can directly observe, as do heavy organic molecules and all other material objects. Research has primarily been focused on investigating superposition on the micro scale, but studies are moving into investigating these properties in larger molecules and even organisms such as viruses. [8]

Tunneling: Objects must have greater kinetic energy to pass through a barrier than the given barrier. Quantum tunneling allows for the possibility of particles to tunnel through a barrier—depending on its height, width, and shape. Tunneling is common among electrons and protons but hasn't been observed with larger compounds such as amino acids or proteins. The size of these larger compounds reduces the probability that this quantum effect will occur. Electron tunneling is used widely in the processes of photosynthesis, cellular respiration, and DNA electron transport. [8]

In order to understand quantum tunneling, one has to let go of the particle concept—envisioning a tiny speck of something (electron, molecule, protein) trying to penetrate a barrier and instead consider an array of possible routes—what's called a smear—in front of, inside, and behind the barrier. The location of this smear isn't really relevant but is used for the sake of discussion.

At some point during the process of tunneling, an observation is made. Who, you ask, is making the observation? The barrier is making the observation. From the cloud of possibilities, a decision is made, and the particle manifests on the other side of the barrier.

You're wondering how an inanimate object like a barrier can make any kind of observation, which implies consciousness. Consider a mitochondrium, which has an internal structure of barriers with which to hold electrons. The barriers can be seen as part of the mitochondrium's consciousness. The mitochondrium uses electrons to produce ATP, the energy currency of the body. In the case of a low energy demand, the mitochondrium "decides" to allow electrons to accumulate behind the barriers. Mitochondria are full of internal baffles (compartments), and each compartment is at a higher energy gradient. When the energy demand is high, a decision could be made by the mitochondria to allow tunneling to occur so the electrons end up on the other side of the barriers, which means more energy at a faster rate of production. [8]

This brings us full circle to the question I raised in the first chapter of this book: Where do you believe your consciousness resides—solely in your head, or is your entire body permeated with consciousness?

Biological processes in living organisms allow for countless chemical bonds to form and break each day as part of the natural functioning of any organism. The rate of formation and destruction of these chemical bonds is determined by the organism's micro environmental needs such as temperature and the enzymatic agents involved in the process. Research is now focusing on the role of quantum tunneling in the creation and destruction of chemical bonds.

Quantum entanglement: Quantum entanglement describes an extension of quantum superposition to more than one object or property, such that two objects or properties are connected.

An entangled system is defined as one in which the quantum state can't be factored in as a product of the states of its local constituents; that is to say, the entangled systems aren't individual particles but are an inseparable whole. In entanglement, one constituent can't be fully described without considering the other(s). Note that the state of a composite system is always expressible as a sum, or superposition, of products of states of local constituents; by definition, the system is entangled if this sum has more than one term. The sum is expressed not as a one-number term but more like 1+1+1. [11]

This quantum phenomenon can be a nonlocal event. This means that when an entangled quantum entity at a certain location in the universe is observed—and therefore influenced—to adopt some particular quantum characteristic, its entangled quantum partner, which may be on the other side of the universe, will instantaneously be influenced to adopt a corresponding characteristic. [11]

Various types of interactions can result in entangled quantum systems. There are ways in which entanglement may be achieved for experimental purposes. Entanglement is broken when the entangled particles decohere through interaction with the environment—for example, when a measurement is made. [11]

We can better observe the special property of entanglement if we separate the two particles involved. Let's say we put one of them in a laboratory in California and the other in a laboratory on a space station orbiting the earth (this was an actual experiment). If we measure a particular characteristic of one of these particles (spin, for example), obtain a result, and then measure the other particle using the same criterion (spin along the same axis), we find the result of the measurement of the second particle will match (in a complementary sense) the result of the measurement of the first particle—they will be opposite in their values. [11]

This is a far cry from what we'd intuit from a classical physics standpoint. A classical system has definite values for all observables throughout the experiment, while the quantum system doesn't. In the example above, the spatially separated entangled quantum system seems to acquire a probability distribution for the outcome of a measurement of the spin along any axis of the other particle upon measurement of the first particle. This probability distribution is, in general, different from what it would be without the measurement of the first particle. [11]

Quantum coherence: Quantum coherence is generally understood as 'wholeness,' a correlation over space and time— for example, atoms vibrating in phase, teams rowing in synchrony in a boat race, choirs singing in harmony, and troops marching in highly regimented formation all conform to our ordinary notion of coherence. [11]

Quantum coherence implies all this and more. Imagine a group of superb musicians sitting down and playing jazz together, where each player is freely improvising from moment to moment and yet keeping in tune and rhythm with the spontaneity of the whole. Quantum coherence is just such a special kind of wholeness, which maximizes both local freedom and global cohesion. [11]

Another vivid and apropos example is the human body, which is an amazing hive of electromagnetic energy playing out over most, if not all, of the 73 octaves of the electromagnetic spectrum—appearing locally as completely chaotic and yet perfectly coordinated as a whole. [11]

The heart has been described as "the most powerful generator of rhythmic information patterns" in the body, acting as the "global conductor in the body's symphony to bind and synchronise the entire system." [12] The heart's beating rhythms not only affect physical health in the obvious sense but also significantly influence perception and understanding.

Indeed, the influence of the heart's rhythm is felt all the way down to the molecular machines in our cells, which are assembled through coherence and vibrating in phase. Mae-Wan Ho, in *The Rainbow and the Worm,* has described it eloquently: "This exquisite music is played in endless variations subject to our changes of mood and physiology, each organism and species with its own repertoire. It would be wonderful if we could tune in and discover how some of us are made of Schubert, and others of Beethoven, or Bach, or something entirely different, which I have called Quantum Jazz." [12]

Decoherence: Decoherence occurs when the quantum characteristics of a particle are lost through an exchange between the quantum system and its environment, which can occur as a result of measurement. In other words, quantum coherence disappears in the act of a measurement. Decoherence theory states: the act of measurement on a quantum superposition state will create entanglement between the system and the meter. [13]

Decoherence versus coherence. One of the ongoing debates within the scientific community argues against quantum effects occurring within biological systems due to decoherence. Biomolecular systems are considered very noisy, meaning they're wet, warm environments with many different electromagnetic systems operating at different frequencies. In contrast, quantum experiments are done under well-controlled conditions in almost perfectly isolated systems, and therefore quantum coherence and entanglement can be manipulated. However, quantum effects also occur within biological systems. Vision is one example. It's a question of how, during the evolutionary process, Nature handled the interplay of noise and quantum coherence to create the optimal operation of biological systems.

Quantum resonance: Quantum resonance is a phenomenon in which a vibrating system or external force drives another system to oscillate with greater amplitude at specific frequencies. Resonance phenomena occur with all types of waves, including the light waves that come to us from the sun. [14] Waves have energy. The wave function, as defined by quantum mechanics, refers to a packet of vibrations. We may envision everything in the universe as made up of waves.

Any specific thing whatsoever isn't just represented by but is, in fact, a group of oscillations measured as sine waves. These groups of sine waves represent all phenomena including particles, atoms, planets, galaxies, thoughts, words, concepts or ideas, and mind. These waveforms may be immensely complex, comprising waves in fractal groups extending into higher dimensions in which their phase relationship is of key importance.

In quantum physics, a wave function is a mathematical description of a system's quantum state. It's not a like a wave in the ocean or a sound wave. All of these wave functions contain information. The vibrations of the wave function comprise not only energy but probabilities.

Consider the human body, which is densely packed with molecules of water, proteins, enzymes, etc., which are all vibrating at many different frequencies. How do self-assembling, molecular machines such as proteins and enzymes accomplish their assemblage in this crowded environment? One solution is looking for compatible resonant frequencies. This will be discussed in greater detail in the next chapter on the quantum body.

Quantum theory has exploded our understanding of the natural sciences. According to the standard interpretation of this theory, a transempirical (transcending human experience) domain of reality exists that doesn't consist of material things but of transmaterial forms (i.e., the quantum view of reality). Even though these forms are transempirical, they're real because they have the potential to manifest themselves in the empirical world. Thus, physical reality appears to us in two domains: potentiality and actuality. Physics posits that the forms in the realm of potentiality are waves–potentiality waves. [15] Since the waves are contiguous, the nature of reality is that of an indivisible wholeness in which all things are interconnected. [16]

Based on this understanding, a microphysical object can exist in a state that isn't a state of actuality but of potentiality, where there is something "standing in the middle between the idea of an event and the actual event," as expressed by Werner Karl Heisenberg, one of the pioneers of quantum mechanics. The middle area Heisenberg refers to might apply to the notion of morphic fields—patterns that are not themselves physical but from which physical manifestation follows. [17] In psychological terminology, we may we refer to these patterns as thoughtforms. [18] Sheldrake and others have found empirical evidence for the existence of such fields. [17]

The idea is that morphic fields are present at the level of the paraphysical substrate (the energetic templates that form the biological structure) from whence they shape physical, space-time manifestation. Not only can they be selected, they can also be created by volition acting at the level of deep consciousness. [19]

Zero-point energy. In quantum field theory, the vacuum state is the quantum state with the lowest possible energy; it contains no physical particles. This is the energy of the ground state. It's mindboggling to try to conceive of the cold vacuum of outer space. When we try, we envision an unimaginably cold, silent, dark vastness in which not a single living thing could survive. However, outer space is full of energy, in particular, electromagnetic radiation in the form of light. [20]

This is also called the zero-point energy—the energy of a system at a temperature of zero. Quantum mechanics states that, even in their ground state, all systems still maintain fluctuations and have an associated zero-point energy as a consequence of their wave-like nature. This means that a particle cooled down to absolute zero will still exhibit vibrations to some extent. [20]

As we've discussed, all objects in the universe have some particle characteristics–they can be detected as discrete entities at a specific location–and some wave characteristics–they can show interference effects and extend over some range in location. The need to have both of these properties at once places tight restrictions on what is and isn't possible for that particular object. The best-known consequence of this is the uncertainty principle, but it's also the basis for the zero-point energy. The uncertainty principle states that, for a given particle, one can't know both its position and its momentum at the same time. [20]

For an object like an electron to have both wave and particle properties, it must have a wavelength associated with it. This wavelength is related to the momentum of the electron. Because zero-point energy is the energy associated with a particle in the lowest possible energy state, and since momentum is related to energy, low energy means low momentum, which means long wavelength. If we want the lowest-energy state for a particle, we're looking for the longest wavelength possible, because this expends less energy. [20]

Everything everywhere has a zero-point energy—from particles to electromagnetic fields and any other type of field, including outer space. Combine them all together and you have the vacuum energy, or the energy of all fields in space. [20]

This would seem to imply that a vacuum state—or simply a vacuum—isn't empty at all but rather the ground-state energy of all fields in space, which may collectively be called the zero-point field (ZPF). The vacuum state contains, according to quantum mechanics, fleeting electromagnetic waves and virtual particles that pop into and out of existence at a whim. So, we must then ask, can this energy be measured, or even calculated? [20]

One calculation puts the energy of a cubic centimeter of empty space at around a trillionth of an erg. This is incomprehensibly tiny, given that an erg has been described as "approximately the amount of work done (or energy consumed) by one common house fly performing one 'push up.'" [21]. Imagine one trillionth of that. Not much, but collect that over all of space, and you still get infinity of energy.

Another derivation of the ZPF is found, as mentioned before, in the uncertainty principle. This uncertainty relates to the inherent quantum fuzziness of energy and matter due to it wavelike nature. It's not possible to know that a particle is lying motionless at the bottom of its potential well. For example, earth is a gravity well and, if an object is lying on the earth, it's more dense than if it were orbiting above the earth. To know if a particle is motionless, we'd have to know both its position and energy with absolute certainty, meaning there's always some movement, some energy. [20]

So, the lowest possible energy of a given system must be greater than the minimum potential of the well—its zero-point energy. This leads us to postulate the collective potential of all particles everywhere with their individual zero-point energies merging into one universal zero-point field. [20]

I've presented these theories and some of the scientific research in this particular area of quantum physics as a way to lay the groundwork for attempting to explain how the mind, brain, and brain waves initiate transactions in the natural world—how our thoughts commingle with everything else and cause matter to manifest in our lives. We're the consciousness that collapses the wave function to create our reality. We'll go into this more fully in later chapters.

Mounting evidence seems to indicate that every physical object (both living and nonliving) has its own unique resonant holographic memory, and this holographic image is stored in the zero-point field. [22] Information in the ZPF is stored nonlocally and can't be attenuated. In addition, this information can be picked up via the mechanism of resonance, as we discussed above.

This information, its storage, and its access is collectively called the quantum hologram (QH). We can think of an organism's QH as its nonlocal information store in the ZPF that's created from all the quantum emissions of every atom, molecule, and cell in the organism. Every objective or physical experience, along with every subjective experience, is stored in our own personal hologram, and we're in constant resonance with it. Each of us has our own unique resonant frequencies or our unique QH, which acts as a "fingerprint" to identify our nonlocal information stored in the zero-point field. [23]

We might be asking ourselves, as observers, are we generating our own reality and therefore our own destiny. If you've seen the movie "The Matrix," you may remember that Neo (played by Keanu Reeves) lives in a simulated world until he's offered a way out, a way back into "reality." This raises a question: If you know you're creating your own reality, would you change it? Would you give up those rich indulgences you so enjoy in order to live in a reality outside of your control?

There's a scene in "The Matrix" in which Cypher (Joe Pantoliano) and Agent Smith (Hugo Weaving) plan to betray Neo. In the scene, Cypher and Agent Smith are dining in an elegant restaurant. Cypher has ordered steak.

Their meal arrives and Agent Smith asks, "Do we have a deal?"

Before Cypher takes the first bite of his steak, he regards the morsel of meat on his uplifted fork and comments that he knows the steak isn't real and that it's the Matrix telling him it will be tender and delicious.

Agent Smith regards him passively.

"After nine years," says Cypher, "you know what I realize?" Cypher then places the bite of steak into his mouth and chews, sighing with pleasure. "Ignorance is bliss."

"Then we have a deal," says Smith.

"I don't want to remember nothing. Nothing, you understand?" states Cypher. "I don't want to be rich, but maybe someone important. Like an actor," (which introduces another layer of the Matrix, since it's an actor stating he wants to be an actor.)

"Whatever you want," purrs Agent Smith.

The scene depicts someone who's seen the real world (with its potential for freedom) and yet desires to return to the bondage of the Matrix. Cypher reflects that aspect of ourselves that desires to remain ignorant and complacent, so we can continue to be "happy"—or at least not stressed by unknown challenges. Cypher desires mindless pleasure over thoughtful existence. What would we choose if offered Morpheus's red pill of knowledge, freedom, and the (sometimes painful) truth of reality or the blue pill of security and blissful ignorance?

In the next chapter, we'll move our discussion from the quantum world to our quantum body.

References:

1. Rosenblum, Bruce. (October 2011). Quantum Physics of Consciousness (Kindle Locations 377-379). Cosmology Science Publishers. Kindle Edition.
2. Quantum. (n.d.). Retrieved from https://www.thefreedictionary.com/quantum
3. Vedral, Vlatko. Decoding Reality: The Universe as Quantum Information (Oxford Landmark Science) (p. 204). OUP Oxford. Kindle Edition.
4. Rosenblum, Bruce, ibid., Kindle Locations 4334-4339.
5. Graham Smetham. (17 April 2010). Quantum Buddhism: Dancing In Emptiness - Reality Revealed at the Interface of Quantum Physics and Buddhist Philosophy (Kindle Location 1190). Lulu.com. Kindle Edition.
6. Ibid., Kindle Location 3481.
7. Schwartz JM, Stapp HP, Beauregard M. Quantum physics in neuroscience and psychology: a neurophysical model of mind–brain interaction. *Philosophical Transactions of the Royal Society B: Biological Sciences*. 2005;360(1458):1309-1327. doi:10.1098/rstb.2004.1598
8. Ball, P. (2017, February 16). Earth - The strange link between the human mind and quantum physics. Retrieved from http://www.bbc.com/earth/story/20170215-the-strange-link-between-the-human-mind-and-quantum-physics
9. Weizmann Institute of Science (27 Feb 1998). "Quantum Theory Demonstrated: Observation Affects Reality". *Science Daily*.
10. Observer effect (physics). (2018, April 22). Retrieved April 22, 2018, from https://en.wikipedia.org/wiki/Observer_effect_(physics)
11. Quantum entanglement. (n.d.). Retrieved April 22, 2018, from https://en.wikipedia.org/w/index.php?title=Quantum_entanglement&oldid=837424113
12. Ho, Mae-Wan. (1993) The Rainbow and the Worm: The Physics of Organisms (pp. 129-130). World Scientific Publishing. Kindle Edition.

13. Arndt, Markus, et al. (1 Nov 2009). Quantum physics meets biology. https://arxiv.org/pdf/0911.0155.pdf
14. Resonance. (2018, April 15). Retrieved April 22, 2018, from https://en.wikipedia.org/w/index.php?title=Resonance&oldid=836547462
15. Villars, C. N. (1987). Microphysical objects as 'potentiality waves.'" European Journal of Physics 8:148–49.
16. Rosenblum, Bruce, ibid. Kindle Locations 1511-1516.
17. Sheldrake, Rupert (1988). The Presence of the Past: Morphic Resonance and the Habits of Nature. Collins, London
18. Barušs, I. (1996). Authentic Knowing: The Convergence of Science and Spiritual Aspiration. Purdue University Press, West Lafayette, US.
19. Rosenblum, Bruce, ibid., Kindle Locations 2239-2243.
20. Baksa, P. (2011, October 03). The Zero Point Field: How Thoughts Become Matter? Retrieved from https://www.huffingtonpost.com/peter-baksa/zero-point-field_b_913831.html
21. Filippenko, Alex, *Understanding the Universe* (of *The Great Courses*, on DVD), Lecture 44, time 24:30, The Teaching Company, Chantilly, VA, USA, 2007.
22. Marcer, P., Schempp, W. (1997). Model of the Neuron Working by Quantum Holography, Informatica Vol. 21, pp. 519-534.

23. Rosenblum, Bruce, ibid. Kindle Locations 3936-3942

Chapter 5
Our Quantum Body

"The cosmos is within us. We are made of star-stuff. We are a way for the universe to know itself."

— *Carl Sagan*

In Chapter 2, we learned about Atwater's discoveries, which revealed more energy is being produced in the body than can be accounted for by simple thermodynamics (food + water + oxygen in and work + heat loss + waste material out). In this chapter, we'll examine where that surplus energy is coming from and how the body produces it.

Here are some questions to consider as we move into this discussion, questions that science hasn't addressed, and which would explain the apparent insufficiencies in the energy required for these particular actions to be possible:

- How do we see "instantly?"
- How are memories recalled instantly?
- Where is our consciousness located, and how is it able to undertake complex reasoning and produce emotional responses?

The energy necessary for our bodies to function is ATP (adenosine triphosphate), a complex organic chemical found in all life forms. [1] ATP is manufactured by the mitochondria, which are power plants within the cells. It's truly remarkable how energy is available to us whenever and wherever we need it—and in adequate amounts for each specific need and action. To contract a muscle, the chemical energy stored in ATP is converted into mechanical energy. Nerve impulses are powered by ATP, and ATP powers the phenomenon of vision, in which light photons strike structures in the eye and these stimuli are converted (by ATP) to nerve impulses. Moreover, this energy is supplied at close to 100% efficiency. [2]

In the synthesis of ATP, carbon compounds in the mitochondria are oxidized into carbon dioxide and water in a process called respiration. If this was a typical chemical reaction taking place outside a living organism, it would be only 10% to 30% efficient, at best. Also, we'd literally burn out because of all the heat generated. Our biology clearly depends on the processes of chemistry and the molecular interactions of chemistry, which are incontrovertibly determined by quantum processes.

Why It's Hard to Believe Quantum Mechanics is Real

Our intuition may tell us to dismiss the strange and unfamiliar elements of quantum mechanics as illusion and claim, "It's all nonsense; the world just isn't like that!" But quantum mechanics has withstood the rigors of thousands of experiments for nearly three quarters of a century. It underpins the technology of our modern world in applications as varied as computers, telecommunications, lasers, compact disks, and medical imaging. If quantum mechanics was fundamentally wrong, we'd know its flaws by now. Our computers wouldn't work, our CDs wouldn't play, and experiments would give inexplicable results. [3]

In addition, if one understands and accepts (meaning, letting go of the classical view of the world) that quantum processes are occurring in the body, the task of explaining consciousness is simplified, which makes it's easier to grasp how habituated thoughts can impact our health and longevity.

Starting Small—Understanding Our Quantum Body

OK, let's get started in the investigation of our quantum body. The atoms that make up our eyes, our brain, our hands, and the elements of the bodies of every other living organism must obey quantum laws. Our view of the world and everything in it is an illusion. Yep, it's an illusion because all objects big enough for us to see are comprised of billions of invisible atoms and molecules, which are continuously in motion. This muddle of incoherent motion dissipates the quantum phenomena of coherence, superposition, and uncertainty. The quantum level of reality is still there but hidden behind a veil of decoherence. [4]

An easy way to think about coherence is to consider two wave sources that have a constant phase difference and the same frequency. The two waves would be considered perfectly coherent and would allow for a large amount of information to be carried—which is what could be assumed to be occurring in our brain to drive consciousness.

Under the classical view of physics inside cells (a view still held by most biologists), the particles within the cell pursued independent movements throughout intracellular spaces. This understanding was the bases for biochemists and geneticists to dissect the cell into smaller and smaller pieces to develop a more thorough understanding. However, now that we have reached the most fundamental particles within cells, we have to look at the quantum cell. Particles cannot be thought of as independent entities but as products of internal measurement. With quantum mechanics, biologists have to take a step away from the fundamental particles and look at the environment in which they're being measured. [5]

Let's take a specific example that will give you an idea of the magnitude of the issue we're trying to describe. We'll first define some general nerve impulse speeds. In the human context, the signals carried by the large-diameter, myelinated neurons that link the spinal cord to muscles can travel at speeds ranging from 70-120 meters per second (m/s) (156-270 miles per hour [mph]), while signals traveling along the same paths carried by the small-diameter, unmyelinated fibers do so at speeds ranging from 0.5-2 m/s (1.1-4.4 mph). Most neurons aren't in physical contact with other neurons. Instead, most signals are passed via neurotransmitter molecules that travel across the small spaces between the nerve cells called synapses. This process takes more time (at least 0.5 m/s per synapse), which slows down the overall speed if the signal is continually passed within a single neuron. So, for purposes of this discussion, let's use 120/mph as an average nerve-impulse speed. [6]

Now, consider you're watching an accomplished pianist perform. To help set the stage for this discussion, I've included a YouTube link to a performance by a famous European pianist, Valentina Lisitsa:

https://www.youtube.com/watch?v=zucBfXpCA6s

[Credit: http://www.valentinalisitsa.com/].

Her performance seems remarkable, considering the speed and complexity of her hand movements, but how remarkable is it really?

Explaining the Quantum Body Using a Musical Prodigy

Let's break it down to the molecular dynamics involved. The pianist learned this piece by reading musical notes on a score. She's accessing memory to recall those notes and tempo while her brain is sending nerve impulses to activate muscle groups throughout her body to play the notes—all occurring on the order of nanoseconds. Additionally, there's a feedback mechanism going on through her sense of hearing as she makes minute adjustments to the tempo and loudness of her playing. On top of all this, the musical piece is emotionally

98

moving for our pianist, and she incorporates her emotions into her performance.

At the molecular level, what went on with our pianist as she read the musical score when she was first learning this complex selection? The eye is an exquisitely sensitive organ. In some species, the eye is able to detect when a single photon, or quantum of light, falls on the retina. The photon is absorbed by a molecule of rhodopsin, a light-sensitive protein located in the outer segment of each rod (a specialized cell in the retina). This results in a nervous impulse coming from the other end of the rod, with an energy at least a million times what was in the photon. The amplification of the incoming photon is, in part, understood as a typical "molecular cascade" of reactions. First, the specific receptor protein, rhodopsin, absorbs a photon and activates many molecules of a second protein, transducin. Each of these activates a molecule of the enzyme phosphodiesterase to split even more molecules of cyclic guanosine monophosphate (cGMP). cGMP normally keeps sodium ion channels open in the otherwise impermeable cell membrane. When it is split, noncyclic GMP is unable to keep the sodium channels open. This makes the sodium channels close up. Sodium ions are kept out of the cell, which leads to an increased electrical polarization of the cell membrane (an increase from about -40 mV to -70 mV), which is sufficient to initiate the nerve impulse to create vision. [7]

We see the world around us in color. What creates color? Put simply, color is the frequency (the speed of oscillation) of the electromagnetic wave that light is. If a wave vibrates more rapidly, the light is bluer. If it vibrates a little more slowly, the light is redder. Color, as we perceive it, is the psychophysical reaction of the nerve signal generated by the receptors of our eyes, which distinguish electromagnetic waves of different frequencies. We'll talk more about how these electromagnetic waves affect us later in this chapter. [8]

There are notable incongruities in the above discussion. For one thing, adding up each of the component steps involved in vision is much larger than how fast visual perception in the central nervous system works, which is on the order of 10^{-1} seconds (s). Activating just one molecule of phosphodiesterase takes 10^{-2} seconds. Furthermore, much of the amplification occurs in the first step, where a single, photon-excited rhodopsin molecule passes on its excitation energy to 500 or more molecules of transducin within one millisecond. How that's achieved is still a mystery. We do know that rhodopsin and transducin molecules are bound to a common membrane, so we assume this membrane plays a critical role in amplifying and transferring long-range, quantum, coherent excitation. [6] Clearly, there are problems in explaining the amount of energy transferred based on currently accepted molecular models.

The Quantum Explanation of Muscle Movement

Next, let's examine what's happening at the level of the pianist's muscles. Our pianist is using her skeletal muscles, which are attached to tendons and bones. These muscles are under her voluntary control as she plays the keys and works the foot pedals of the piano. About 40% of our muscle mass is skeletal muscle, i.e., muscle attached to bones, like those in our arms, legs, and trunk. Another 5% to 10% of our muscle mass is smooth muscles such as those in the gut, body wall, and heart. [9]

Skeletal muscle consists of bundles of long, thin fibers, which are large enough to identify with a magnifying glass. These fibers are several centimeters in length, and each fiber is actually a giant cell made from fusing many cells together. A single muscle fiber, magnified a hundred times or more under a light microscope, is seen to be comprised of a bundle of 20 to 50 much smaller fibers, or myofibrils, each of which is 1 to 2 μm (micrometer, one-millionth of a meter) in diameter. A myofibril

100

has regular, 2.5-μm repeating units, called sarcomeres, along its length. Myofibrils are lined up next to each other so that their sarcomeres register. Under much higher magnifications (thousands to tens of thousands of magnitudes) of an electron microscope, we see extremely regular arrays of these periodic structures. [9]

We also see that each sarcomere consists of alternating thin and thick filaments. These filaments are made up of the two main muscle proteins, actin and myosin, with actin making up thin filaments and myosin making up thick filaments. Contraction occurs as the actin filaments surrounding the myosin filaments slide past each other, like a treadmill. The study of the detailed structure of resting as well as contracting muscle has utilized X-ray crystallography. The actin and myosin molecules are packed closely together, and the precise arrangement looks almost like crystal formations. [10]

On each myosin filament, there are 624 myosin-head groups. Upon muscle contraction, each sarcomere in the muscle shortens proportionately. Thus, when a myofibril containing a chain of 20,000 sarcomeres contracts from 5 cm to 4 cm, each sarcomere shortens correspondingly from 2.5 μm to 2 μm. The energy for this contraction is derived from the hydrolysis of ATP. [10]

Muscle contraction is triggered by a quick electrical discharge at the site where a nerve impinges on the muscle-cell membrane. This electrical discharge followed by recovery to the baseline electrical potential is called action potential. The muscle contraction releases calcium ions, Ca2+, from within the cell to initiate contraction simultaneously throughout the entire cell within a millisecond. [11]

Contraction is a complex process where individual myosin heads attach and detach to the finding sites on the actin filaments at the rate of 50 cycles or more per second—each of which requires the transfer of energy contained in one molecule of ATP—precisely coordinated over the whole cell. [12,13] In a typical muscle contraction, all the muscle cells—billions, at the very least—execute the same molecular process together.

For our pianist, simply moving her fingers over the keys and moving her hands to create different chords is a feat requiring a series of actions coordinated instantaneously. These movements span nine orders of magnitude from 10^{-19} meter (nanometer=one billionth of a meter)—which represents the intermolecular spacing between the actin and myosin heads—to about one meter (slightly longer than the length of our pianist's arm). Each action, furthermore, involves the coordinated splitting of 1,019 individual molecules of ATP to have enough energy to complete these processes. [14]

Traditional scientific viewpoints aren't adequate to explain how our pianist accomplishes her performance. At best, energy transduction can only occur at the efficiency of a typical chemical reaction outside living organisms, which, as we've mentioned, is between 10% to 30% efficiency. If that was the full explanation, our pianist's body would generate so much heat that she would burn out. However, she didn't burn out from heat exhaustion, and we want to understand why this is so. The coordination between her eyes, consciousness, and hand movement depends on our biological subsystems being inherently coherent so instantaneous intercommunication can occur. That being said, there simply isn't enough time between one musical phrase and the next for sensory inputs to be sent to the brain and comprehended for coordinated outputs to be sent back to the hands. So, what gives?

We're Crystalline Beings

It's been recognized for decades that all the major constituents of living organisms are liquid crystals. The liquid crystals in your computer screen and TV monitors are what display the images.

Living organisms are composed of liquid crystalline networks. The lipids of cellular membranes, the DNA in chromosomes, and possibly all proteins—especially cytoskeletal proteins, muscle proteins, and proteins in the connective tissues such as collagens and proteoglycans (macromolecules that are part protein and part carbohydrate)—are liquid crystals. [15]

A mesophase is a state of matter intermediate between liquid and solid. Gelatin is a common example. The collagen-rich, liquid crystalline mesophases in connective tissues have structured water associated with them. This creates a semi-conducting, highly responsive network that extends throughout the organism. This network is directly linked to the intracellular matrices of individual cells via proteins and water channels penetrating the cell membrane, so the connective tissues and intracellular matrices are able to form a global tensegrity (tensional integrity) system together as well as an excitable electrical continuum for rapid intercommunication throughout the body. [16]

It's All About Electromagnetism

If one has a classical physics worldview, the idea that we're comprised of liquid crystals may seem somewhat surprising. It may be helpful to shift our focus of viewing the body as a solid to an alternative understanding that even though our bodies (and most other things in our environment) appear solid, we're comprised of molecules—which are mostly empty space (think planets orbiting the sun)—bound together by electromagnetic forces. Even though we're made up of molecules that are mostly empty space, we appear to have density. In the classical world, we're solid "mass," but, in the quantum world, we're millions of atoms and molecules jostling around in constant movement, with vast spaces between them, held in place by electromagnetic forces. "We" exist in both states, yet each perceives us differently.

The force we call electromagnetism holds together the matter that forms solid bodies—it holds together atoms in molecules and electrons in atoms. This is the basis of chemistry and all living matter. It's this force that operates in the neurons of our brain, governs our processing of the information coming in from the world we perceive, and influences the way we think. It's this same force that creates the friction that stops a sliding object, turns electric motors and combustion engines, or allows us to turn on lights and talk on our cell phones.

The speed of electromagnetic energy signals is 186,000 miles per second—the speed of light. The relationship between the speed of electromagnetic energy and the speed of light brings us into the realm of being able to account for the dynamic processes occurring in our pianist—vision, cognition, and transmission of information to muscles.

The idea that molecules communicate and exchange energy via electromagnetic resonance fits perfectly with the growing research that cells are liquid crystals, so that all molecules—including the 70% of our bodies that's made up of water—are aligned and working coherently together.

More importantly, vibrational energy can be transferred over large distances—theoretically, infinite distances—if the energy is radiated in the same way that solar energy or vibrations from a tuning fork radiate. Even though electromagnetic radiations are able to move at the speed of light, in practice, the speed may be slower because of absorption by the intervening medium. [17]

The Role of Body Consciousness

Body consciousness possesses all the definitions of "consciousness"—sentience, intercommunication, and memory. Body consciousness is distributed throughout the entire liquid crystalline matrix that connects each single cell to every other. Brain consciousness is both embedded in to body consciousness and is coupled with it. [18]

It's been hypothesized that the coordination of instantaneous (nonlocal) body functions is mediated by the body consciousness existing in the liquid crystal structures of the body. This idea is dependent on the idea that living systems have a special kind of coherence—quantum coherence—that belongs to macroscopic quantum systems. The unity of experience, or, the "unity of intentionality" [19], arises from and depends on quantum coherence, which creates succession(s) of overlapping simultaneities that segments and binds serial sensations into a seamless whole. [20]

There's not much diffusion in this suggested system. Instead, energy transfer—by molecular resonance or coherent excitations—probably occurs across large distances. Even molecules that are in different parts of the cell or body can be activated. When entire populations of similar molecules are activated, long-range coordination of function can happen instantaneously. [21]

We know that Nature is inherently nonlocal in its behavior. In a positive light, there are instantaneous connections or correlations among the parts of physical systems—true instantaneous action-at-a-distance that has been well-studied. [22]

It's worth repeating that the interconnections we're discussing are different from those in classical physics, which are limited by the speed of light. We're talking about instantaneous interconnections. These quantum correlations reveal that Nature is non-causally unified in ways we only dimly understand. [22]

Mitochondria can behave as individual oscillators whose dynamics may obey collective network properties. In your heart muscles, the cardiomyocytes will synchronize to oscillate with high amplitudes and sustain these oscillations within the mitochondrial network. [23] In other words, the mitochondrial networks of cardiomyocytes functions as one highly coordinated network of oscillators. This means each mitochondrion is able to affect the temporal behavior of its neighbors, so the entire collective of mitochondria in cardiac cells work like a network. [24]

What we see in living systems is that both quantum coherence and resonance occur, and this accounts for the instantaneous transmission of information and energy. Recall that resonance is when two wave sources are perfectly coherent, which means they have a constant phase difference, the same frequency, and the same waveform. Resonance results in a vibrating system or an external force that causes another system to oscillate at a specific frequency but with a greater amplitude.

Another feature of current quantum theory is that when coherent wave functions experience "entanglement," there can be an immediate transmission of information from one resonant component to another—i.e., the distance between the components is no object. Erwin Schrödinger defined entanglement as a situation in which the experimenter's frame of reference and the system under study can only be regarded as an inseparable whole. [25]

Our living system is so thoroughly dynamic that each cell in the body is simultaneously crisscrossed by many circuits of flow, each circuit with its own time domain and direction specified by local pumping, gating, and chemical transformation. As a result, classical equilibrium constants are quite irrelevant, because each "constant" is, in reality, a continuous function of variables including flow rates, electrical and mechanical field intensities, and so on. [26]

Returning to our pianist, let's discuss the amount of energy required to handle all the dynamics involved in her performance.

Energy production in the body at the molecular level is handled by the mitochondria. These cellular energy factories are able to channel energy from glucose or fats harvested from food into electrons. These high-energy electrons are then shuffled through a cascade of reactions to make ATP, the molecule that fuels most cellular work. Conventionally, biological models describe the electrons as hopping from molecule to molecule within mitochondria, but—once again—this simple picture can't account for the speed at which ATP is generated.

Electron tunneling is the process of going "under" an energy barrier via an overlap of the quantum mechanical wave functions of the electron in different, neighboring states. Electron tunneling is involved in the separation of charges and electron transport such as cytochrome c, which is part of Complex IV of the Electron Transport Chain, a large transmembrane protein complex found in the mitochondrion. [27] Hydrogen transfer reactions may also involve tunneling across energy barriers via an overlap of quantum mechanical wave functions between enzyme complexes of substrates and products. [28]

A Quantum Solution to a Biological Mystery

A model has been developed to describe how electrons exist within the mitochondria. The high energy electrons exist in a quantum superposition, smeared (smeared is another term for tunneling) out at once across all the molecules in the ATP production line of the mitochondria. Using this model, scientists have performed calculations and predicted a 30% boost in ATP production rate. This is what has been observed in experiments, providing, once again, a quantum solution to a biological mystery of energy production. [29]

It's important to understand the term "smear" as it's used here, because it will occur in our discussion in the next chapter. What's being implied by this term is pretty wild. When you read the above paragraph, perhaps you envisioned a mitochondrion with a cloud over it or maybe a smear over or inside it. Also, because you now have some knowledge of wave-particle duality, you may have considered that this smear would be composed of high-energy electrons in a waveform ready to localize in the mitochondria in the electron transport chain as an electron particle.

However, none of that would be correct. First, we have the locality problem. The smear is nonlocal, meaning it isn't hovering over or inside the mitochondrion. We're actually unable to visualize this. Prior to an actual measurement event, all we can say is that the system is represented by probability amplitudes evolving in an infinite dimensional complex to make it clear that these wave functions or probability amplitudes aren't physical states in any reasonable sense of the term. Prior to detection, the probability amplitude or wave function doesn't exist in space-time and isn't a physical wave with particles like a wave in the ocean. It's a wavelength of probability amplitudes. In quantum mechanics, measurement actually brings about a transformation of an evolving superposition of probabilities that don't exist in physical space-time into an actual space-time event. In addition, prior to their manifestation, the quantum probabilities interfere just like with waves.

What's implied here is that mitochondria have consciousness. An induced measurement observation collapses them into an actual space-time event of increased electron flow through the mitochondrial electron transport chain.

It gets even more odd, because what's also implied is that information spontaneously emerges from emptiness, and we need to fully appreciate this to update how we view reality. Probability amplitudes are information, and they exist in a nonphysical space-time place.

There's speculation that this emptiness is the Zero Point Field (ZPF), which will be discussed in the next chapter. This field is ubiquitous, nonlocal, can't be attenuated, lasts indefinitely (e.g. never loses coherence), can store unlimited quantities of information, and any portion of it encodes the whole just as a hologram does. It can be thought of not only as Nature's information storage mechanism but also as Nature's information transfer mechanism. [30]

Consider the thoughts occurring in your mind right now. They're like probability waves in that they contain no substance. Thoughts just emerge. Some of them contain information you may act on while others are just flotsam in a sea of consciousness. If we have a classical physics background, we may categorize thoughts as random nerve impulses firing in the brain. Even though it may seem the thought is residing "someplace" in our brain, science has never actually found, recorded, or isolated a thought or thoughts.

Living organisms depend on quantum reactions. Not only are the mitochondria involved in quantum tunneling, individual enzymes and other molecules also act as "quantum energy machines." Individual quanta of energy released are directly transferred from the point of release to the point of use and all energy transductions are carried out by these enzymes and molecules. Coordinating all of these activities requires nothing short of quantum coherence, especially when considering the rapid and specific responses, and intercommunication that take place in an organism. [31]

The coherence of organisms is based on superposing coherent activities over all space-time domains. Each of these activities is correlated with one another and with the whole but also independent of the whole. In other words, the quantum coherent state is scalable from the molecular level to the microscopic level to the macroscopic level. This state maximizes both global cohesion and local freedom. It is the foundation for why living systems are sensitive to weak signals and how they are able to intercommunicate and respond quickly. [32]

This brings us full circle to how our pianist was able to accomplish her performance. If we maintain a classical physics view of life, we run into a number of substantial problems regarding the energy and data requirements for her performance. It's only by understanding the quantum state that the performance can be explained.

In quantum physics, Nature and reality are represented by the quantum state. The electromagnetic field of the quantum state is the fundamental entity, the continuum that comprises the inherent oneness and unity of all things. [33]

Quantum Physics and the Human Brain (Consciousness)

We now understand that through the quantum effects of coherence, tunneling, and entanglement, information and energy are transferred at a rate that explains our pianist's magnificent performance, but what we haven't yet discussed is what's happening in her brain.

Since the brain requires mitochondria to fulfill its energy requirements, the same quantum conditions of coherence, tunneling, and entanglement apply to its operation. However, it's been difficult for science to observe these functions in the brain. For one thing, we can't just remove a section of the brain (even a tiny piece) and hope to gain a notion of the complexity of what's occurring. In addition—and this is the more knotty problem—there's the quantum-observer issue, meaning science (a manifestation of our consciousness) is trying to observe itself and, as a result, is affecting (influencing) the collapse of the wave function, which is what creates our reality. This is a problem of objectivity that's especially evident in cases of entanglement.

Our pianist demonstrates two types of mental activity—rote processes and critical thinking. The conscious mind represents only about 10% of our mind's capacity. The other 90% is subconscious—below our level of thought and running automatically. Rote processes kick in once we've learned something and it gets transferred to the subconscious. Driving your car while listening to the radio and simultaneously planning your day's activities is an example of rote processes taking place while you're engaged in conscious thought. In the case of our pianist, she's spent thousands of hours practicing, thus most of her performance is at the level of rote processes. The critical thinking part is her artistic interpretation and expression of the piece.

Now, this is interesting, because the artistic expression of the performance is unique to the pianist. In fact, we can say the performance as a whole is a unique expression of her consciousness; her individuality illuminates her performance. The consciousness aspect of this discussion will be examined in greater detail in the next chapter.

Summary and a Personal Story

This chapter has examined the interrelated nature of processes taking place constantly in our bodies. From the molecular level to the macro level, there are interrelated processes occurring throughout the body, organized in cycles. An example of cycles in living systems are biological rhythms. We can see our own circadian rhythms when we think about our sleeping patterns, but cycles can have a much broader range, which is difficult for us to see. Electrical discharges of single cells may just last for milliseconds, but organisms and their populations have easily viewable circadian and circa-annual cycles. [13] These cycles connect and work off of each other to create a complex, multidimensional, entangled space-time for an organism that's far removed from the simple, linear, Newtonian space and time of mechanical physics.

This chapter has offered some provocative observations to indicate all these rhythms are indeed entangled, correlated, and coupled together in a quantum state.

The fundamental understanding of reality in quantum mechanics is that every alternative possibility available in a system co-exists in a "pure state", not a "mixed state" until the instant that we observe it. We need to differentiate between a "pure" and "mixed" state. A pure state is one of indivisible unity, which we can represent as a superposition of all possible alternatives. A mixed state is one in which different states exist in different proportions. The act of observation *seems* to put an end to this dreamlike pure state and changes it into one of possibilities (chances that a particular action will occur) that previously existed only as a potential (the pure state comprising all possibilities). It seems like the observer is determining the fate of a particle by collapsing all its potentialities into one state of definiteness, hence the parable of Schrödinger's cat. If you're not familiar with this famous quantum conundrum, check out this YouTube video:

https://www.youtube.com/watch?v=OkVpMAbNOAo

There's a school of thought in quantum physics that believes it's the act of observation by human consciousness that makes definite things happen. [34]

As we transition to the next chapter, I want to leave you with an experience from my life. I've practiced aikido for a number of years. Aikido is a form of martial arts, but a good aikidoist would never be engaged in a fight. The whole point about aikido is for the practitioner to step aside when attacked and redirect the opponent's energy. This could be a physical attack or a verbal attack, as in a heated argument when emotions are running high.

When I first started aikido, I found it difficult. There were repetitive drills of hand and foot movements and, when we'd pair up to practice, I'd want to use my physical force to try to stop a punch from landing. That caused me to get hurt a lot, but I persevered.

Traditionally, aikido is taught in an open class in which beginners work with advanced students. Of course, the advanced students loved it when a new student came in and thought he could muscle everyone around. The new student would get pounded, which I did.

I kept practicing, and, over the years, I rose in rank, learning how to step aside and redirect my opponent's energy. But it was still necessary to do the repetitive drills over and over as part of the discipline.

There came a time when I undertook an advanced test at a national conference. As part of the test, there was a section called *randori*, which, simply translated, means, "anything goes!" There are no restrictions on speed or type of attacks. This is the culmination of all that we train for and truly demonstrates how well the practitioner has developed the unification of mind, body, and spirit.

In my test, there were six attackers. Some wielded wooden staffs and others wooden knives, and they were all attacking at once at full speed. In that test, it all came together for me—all those years of repetitive drills. I didn't have to think. I just moved, stepping aside of each punch or knife thrust by redirecting the opponent's energy. It was if I was effortlessly dancing and, perhaps most interesting of all, there was a part of me that was observing myself in this dance. In other words, there was a part of me that had stepped out of my own way and quit trying to control the situation.

I thought about that experience for a number of months before I came to understand that it takes practice to learn to quiet the mind. Of course, I understand it takes practice to learn a skill, but the greatest influence on anything we do is our consciousness, which we'll explore in the next chapter.

References:

1. https://en.wikipedia.org/wiki/Adenosine_triphosphate.
2. Ho, Mae-Wan. *The Rainbow and the Worm: The Physics of Organisms*, p. 11. World Scientific Publishing. Kindle Edition.
3. McFadden, Johnjoe. *Quantum Evolution: Life in the Multiverse*, p. 219. HarperCollins Publishers. Kindle Edition.
4. Ibid., pp. 219-220.
5. Ibid., p. 252.
6. Ho, Ibid., p.8
7. Ho, Mae-Wan., Ibid., p. 7.
8. Rovelli, Carlo. *Reality Is Not What It Seems: The Journey to Quantum Gravity* p. 60. Penguin Publishing Group. Kindle Edition
9. Wikipedia contributors. (2018,March 30)Muscle. In Wikipedia, The Free Encyclopedia. Retrieved 22:55, April 28,2018 from https://en.wikipedia.org/w/index.php?titile=Muscle&oldid=833322400
10. Ho, Mae-Wan. *The Rainbow and the Worm: The Physics of Organisms*. World Scientific Publishing. Kindle Edition, p. 33.
11. Ríos E, Pizarro G.Voltage sensor of excitation-contraction coupling in skeletal muscle. Physiol Rev. 1991 Jul;71(3):849-908.
12. Granzier, H.L.M., Myers, J.A. and Pollack, G.H. (1987). Stepwise shortening of muscle fibre segments. J. Musc. Res. Cell Mot. 8, 242-251.
13. Ho, Mae-Wan. ed. (1995) Bioenergetics, S327 Living Processes, An Open University Third Level Science Course, Open University Press, Milton Keynes.
14. Ho, Mae-Wan. The Rainbow and the Worm. The Physics of Organisms, pp.8-10. World Scientific Publlishing. Kindle Edition.
15. Ho, Mae-Wan. The Rainbow and the Worm: The Physics of Organisms, p. 209. World Scientific Publishing. Kindle Edition
16. Ho, M.W. and Harris, D. The energetics of the four-minute mile, in Bioenergetics Book 2, S327, An Open

University Third level course (M.W. Ho ed.) pp 186-234, Open Univerity Press, Milton Keyes, 1995

17. Ho, Ibid., p. 237.
18. Freeman, Walter J. and John M. Barrie. "Chaotic oscillations and the genesis of meaning in cerebral cortex." (1994).
19. Ho, Mae-Wan. The Rainbow and the Worm: The Physics of Organisms, p. 239. World Scientific Publishing. Kindle Edition
20. Ibid. p. 139
21. Mansfield, Vic. Tibetan Buddhism and Modern Physics: Toward a Union of Love and Knowledge, p. 73. Templeton Press. Kindle Edition.
22. Ibid., p. 88.
23. Aon MA, Cortassa S, O'Rourke B. The Fundamental Organization of Cardiac Mitochondria as a Network of Coupled Oscillators. Biophysical Journal. 2006;91(11):4317-4327. doi:10.1529/biophysj.106.087817.
24. Wallace, B. Alan. Hidden Dimensions: The Unification of Physics and Consciousness (Columbia Series in Science and Religion) (p. 19). Columbia University Press. Kindle Edition.
25. Ho, Mae-Wan. *The Rainbow and the Worm: The Physics of Organisms*. World Scientific Publishing. Kindle Edition, pp. 28-29.
26. Bechtold, R., Kuehn, C., Lepre, C. & Isied, S. S. Directional electron transfer in ruthenium-modified horse heart cytochrome c. Nature 322, 286 (1986).
27. Ho, Mae-Wan The Rainbow and the Worm: The Physics of Organisms, pp. 35-36. World Scientific Publishing. Kindle Edition.
28. L Amico, R Fazio, A Osterloh, V Vedral. Entanglement in many-body systems. Reviews of modern physics 80 (2), 517
29. Rosenblum, Bruce. Quantum Physics of Consciousness (Kindle Locations 4005-4008). Cosmology Science Publishers. Kindle Edition.
30. Ho, Mae-Wan. The Rainbow and the Worm: The Physics of Organisms, p. 285. World Scientific Publishing. Kindle Edition.

31. Ibid., p. 286.
32. Rosenblum, Bruce. Quantum Physics of Consciousness (Kindle Locations 4442-4444). Cosmology Science Publishers. Kindle Edition.
33. Ho, Mae-Wan. The Rainbow and the Worm: The Physics of Organisms, pp. 83-84. World Scientific Publishing. Kindle Edition
34. Ibid., p. 275.

PART TWO: Chapter 6
Spiritual Tradition – Consciousness

"To realize the inexpressible truth, do not manipulate mind or body but simply open into transparency with relaxed, natural grace."

– TILOPA (10TH CENTURY)

Nothing in space is motionless. Gravity causes all objects in the universe—such as stars and galaxies—to attract and "fall" toward each other. These attractive movements occur within the ongoing expansion taking place in the universe. In this way, our Earth is part of a fantastic cosmic ballet. First, the Earth spins us in space at a speed of nearly 20 miles per second during its annual journey around the sun. The sun then pulls the Earth with it during its voyage through the Milky Way at a speed of 140 miles per second. The Milky Way is, in turn, being drawn toward the Andromeda Galaxy (its closest neighbor) at a rate of approximately 55 miles per second. And there's more. The so-called Local Group, which is the galaxy group that contains the Milky Way, is speeding at about 375 miles per second toward the Virgo cluster of galaxies, which is moving toward a large complex of galaxies called the Great Attractor. [1]

Everything in the universe is constantly moving and changing. Nothing is permanent. Movement and impermanence is the nature of reality.

At the level of our everyday experience, our world consists of a myriad of substances we can describe generally as "matter." Matter exists in various states: solid, liquid, and gas. Because we can't see or smell air, and we have no difficulty moving through it, we don't perceive it as matter, even though it is. What makes certain forms of matter have the qualities of solid materiality is that the nuclear and electromagnetic forces are holding together the molecules of which it's comprised in a particular density. In this respect, what we perceive in our experiential world is often completely misleading and deceptive as to its true nature. [2]

This includes our bodies. What we're able to experience with our senses seems real to us, but most of what's out there we're unable to perceive. We're swimming in a vast ocean of waves and frequencies. The mechanism by which these waves and frequencies are conjured into sticks and stones is our consciousness.

Algae as Observer

As we discussed in Part One, there's a growing consensus amongst physicists that quantum "objects" depend, in some way, on the consciousness observing them. [3] More specifically, based on quantum principles, all matter displays the quantum characteristics of entanglement, coherence, correlation, resonance, and consciousness, and these principles are applicable to everything from the micro scale of subatomic particles to the largest objects in the cosmos and everything in between.

Clearly, we're matter and we're also conscious. "Cogito ergo sum:" I think, therefore I am. What's implied here is breathtaking in its implications.

Let's look at a study published in 2010 to expand this discussion. This study, carried out by researchers at the University of Toronto in Ontario, focused on the process of photosynthesis. Photosynthesis is the mechanism by which chlorophyll molecules in plants convert water, carbon dioxide, and sunlight into energy, oxygen, and carbohydrates. Photosynthesis is a vital and fundamental mechanism of life on this planet. The Toronto researchers discovered that the high efficiency of photosynthesis is accomplished because of the quantum mechanics involved. A quantum, wavelike, electronic coherence plays an important role. This wavelike characteristic explains the extreme efficiency of the energy transfer because it enables the system to simultaneously sample all the potential energy pathways and choose the most efficient one. [4]

According to the Toronto researchers, the classical explanation of photosynthesis—which requires the transfer of electrons—is simply "inadequate and inaccurate." What they discovered is that the essential process is one of a sustained, coherent, superposed state of resonant interaction within a quantum wave function. The superposition results in a collapse of possibilities into the most energy-efficient pathway. [5]

This is an extraordinary example of how quantum, superposed wave function is used by a natural mechanism to test all the possibilities before the most efficient one is selected. Stated most simply, a wave function, in quantum physics, is "a mathematical description of the quantum state of a system. The wave function is a complex-valued probability amplitude, and the probabilities for the possible results of measurements made on the system can be derived from it." [6]

In the last chapter, we discussed how a wave function isn't composed of particles or anything we consider real in a classical view. Rather, it consists of probabilities. It's the collapse of the wave function of probabilities that result in the most energy-efficient pathway. An awareness of this collapse of the wave function implies an observer—an observing consciousness.

The research on photosynthesis cited above was done on marine algae, so the observing consciousness was the algae. Now, you may think this is totally preposterous, but consider this: A common dictionary definition of consciousness is "the ability to be aware of and perceive the relationship between oneself and one's environment." The most basic definition of consciousness, however, is simply "awareness."

For the algae, photosynthesis represents food and energy, which drives all its other cellular functions including asexual reproduction. The algae use photosynthesis for survival, and this implies a rudimentary sense of awareness. The understanding we're left with is that awareness (consciousness) permeates all life—from the most primitive single-celled organisms to the most complex life form on the planet—us. Consciousness permeates down to the molecular and atomic levels in the form of self-assembling molecular machines and mitochondria that produce energy for our bodies.

Who or What is Conscious?

If you take a moment and consider this, you may realize you hold a viewpoint that regards one particular life form as conscious and another life form that isn't. However, consciousness is just degrees of awareness. You may consider your dog or cat to be conscious, but what about that magnificent tree in your back yard or those beautiful flowers in your garden that you've been working on all summer? What about the bacteria that give you a sore throat—aware or unaware? In some way, all of these entities are responding to their environment, seeking food, replicating, developing defenses to ward off predators, or managing to survive during droughts or an assault of killer antibiotics.

Quantum physics tells us that any perception (manifestation of consciousness) has an impact upon the quantum realm of the wave function. Simply put, perception collapses the wave function into manifestation. Every organism is making complex decisions as it interacts with its environment.

"Consciousness is an interior aspect or quality of the wave function, which reflexively operates upon the potentialities for experiential existence," stated Graham Smetham in his book, *Quantum Buddhism: Dancing in Emptiness—Reality Revealed at the Interface of Quantum Physics & Buddhist Philosophy.* [7] What this means to us is our thoughts and decisions, manifested within their internal feeling tones (associated emotions), can be thought of as collapsed wave functions. When you have a thought or make a decision, you experience the collapsing wave function inside your individuated consciousness, which creates the inner experience of meaning. Repetitive collapsing of a wave function by consistently making the same decision sets the stage for limiting one's happiness, pleasure, and spontaneity.

Recall that entangled quantum phenomena can instantaneously affect one other over vast cosmic distances. Distance is irrelevant for this kind of entangled mutual determination. [8] This entanglement at a distance has implications for families, communities, countries, and the planet.

Essentially, when looking at the things using orthodox (von Neumann-Heisenberg) quantum mechanics, the material world is represented by the quantum state. This empty state has a characteristic of "potentia," so there are objective probabilities for actual events to happen. As such, this makes the quantum state more mind-like than matter-like. It doesn't just have stored information about the past but also has objective tendencies pertaining to events that haven't yet happened. These include projections into the future and basically imagined ideas of what may happen. Because of this, the physical aspects of quantum mechanics are more like mental thoughts than like material things. [9]

Emptiness denotes a realm of potentiality hovering between existence and non-existence that underlies the possibility (the potentia) of all phenomena.

Quantum mechanics implies that consciousness plays a crucial role in the formation and evolution of the universe as we know it. Yet, most researchers in psychology and brain science regard consciousness as nothing more than a property of the brain, with no significance for the universe at large. The scientific view of Nature as matter obeying laws of physics has been so successful that we easily forget that everything we know of the objective world is by way of human consciousness.

Eastern and Western Views of Consciousness

Currently, the West has no pure science of consciousness to study the nature, origins, and potentials of this natural phenomenon, and it similarly lacks an applied science of consciousness that reveals the means for how consciousness can be refined and enhanced. Even though the West doesn't have a science to understand consciousness, other human civilizations throughout history haven't been as deficient. [10]

Eastern religion and philosophy have a strong core of relational thinking. Buddhism, in particular, contains the notion of "emptiness," which is akin to von Neumann's "empty set" (a mathematical term referring to a set containing no elements). In Buddhism, the term "emptiness" means that things don't exist in themselves but are only possible in relation to other things. [11] For example, consider a wooden chair. What is it, really? The chair is made from parts of a tree that grew from a seed of another tree and required soil, water, and sunlight for it to grow. In other words, emptiness means nothing exists by itself. Everything exists in relation to "other."

Buddhism has developed rigorous methods over its 2500-year history for refining the attention. By applying that attention to explore consciousness, they can seek to understand the origins, nature, and role of consciousness in the natural world. Buddhism's empirical and rational studies and discoveries challenge many of the assumptions of Western thought, particularly that of scientific materialism. [12]

The Meaning of "Emptiness"

"Emptiness, or *shunyata*, is the Buddhist concept of a fundamental, non-substantial, 'empty' ground of potentiality that gives rise to the multitudinous productions within dualistic experience through the operation of a primordial activity of cognition," states Smetham in his book. [13] Common sense, of course, suggests that the idea of an independent, "material" reality is just an artifact of how our mind or consciousness work must be misguided. Before the quantum era of Western science, such an idea would have been regarded as outlandish by classical scientist. With the beginning of the quantum revolution, however, the understanding that the physical world's true nature is mind-substance has become increasingly apparent. And, as it turns out, quantum physics is very much in line with the concept of emptiness as defined in Buddhism.

This brings us back to the perspective that the physical properties of an object are dependent on its relationship to other objects and how it's interconnected with them. The nature of the object doesn't solely lie within itself. The fundamental Buddhist insight into the emptiness of phenomena is that all phenomena are completely and intimately connected to, and even created by, the observer's mind. [12]

Many of the "founding fathers" of quantum mechanics reached the same conclusion. Erwin Schrödinger, who discovered the fundamental quantum equation, for instance, came to the conclusion that, "Mind has erected the objective outside world … out of its own stuff." [14] Max Planck, the physicist who inadvertently began the quantum revolution, came to a similar conclusion: "All matter originates and exists only by virtue of a force… We must assume behind this force the existence of a conscious and intelligent Mind. This Mind is the matrix of all matter," (from Planck's speech, "The Nature of Matter," presented in Florence, Italy, in 1944). [15]

The Reality We Create

The famous British astronomer Arthur Eddington put it this way: "The term 'particle' survives in modern physics, but very little of its classical meaning remains. A particle can now best be defined as the conceptual carrier of a set of variates. It is also conceived as the occupant of a state defined by the same set of variates. It might seem desirable to distinguish the 'mathematical fictions' from 'actual particles,' but it is difficult to find any logical basis for such a distinction." [12]

As previously discussed, at the quantum level, existence itself hovers between existence and non-existence according to the requirement of Heisenberg's uncertainty principle. This is the ground level of reality that the Buddhists call emptiness. As we've seen, this emptiness isn't 'nothingness" but a realm of interdependent potentiality.

Our natural way of dealing with the numerous objects we interact with in everyday life is simply to treat them as if they exist on their own, completely independent of our—and everyone else's—mind. We also assume that each object is self-enclosed, so to speak, and separate from all other objects. This is an innate framework for understanding our physical environment, and it was the framework that underpinned the pre-quantum, classical understanding of the physical world.

The issue of deepest importance here is that this innate perspective on phenomena—a view embedded in the human psyche—relies on the assumption that all objects have some kind of inner core of self-enclosed, independent existence that's all their own, so to speak. It's this innate perception of the way things exist that's called into question by the Buddhist doctrine of emptiness. It's also a view of reality that's now rejected by quantum physics. [16]

Where Are You?

This brings to mind the homunculus argument, which, briefly, refers to a fallacy arising most commonly in the theory of vision.

The argument states that one can explain [human] vision by observing that light is reaching the retinas in the eyes. This creates an image on the retinas, so something (or someone) in the brain can view these like scenes on a movie screen. The assumption here is that there's a "little man" (homunculus) inside the brain who's looking at the movie. The question comes up: What is the nature of that little man? [17] This concept seems really funny to us now, but let's be completely honest. Do you believe you have a unique, independent self that resides somewhere within you? Many of us hold that belief.

Maybe your view is that the unique "you" resides in your whole body, or maybe in your brain or your heart. The question being posed in the context of emptiness is, "Where *do* you reside?" Is it even necessary that you have a place of residence (i.e., a body) to exist? Does that unique you change in any way if you aren't living in that self-enclosed existence? These are contemplative questions, and I encourage you to consider them and their implications.

Here's another exercise to consider: You're at a party and someone invades "your" space. You know what I mean—they're standing too close or talking too loudly, and you feel uncomfortable. Do you back up to re-establish an acceptable boundary, or do you tolerate that person in your space? My point is, your self-enclosed existence already extends a little farther than you may have imagined. Take a risk.... explore this me/not-me boundary.

The Essence of Reality is Interdependence

If we truly explore the nature of reality, we'll never find anything that exists independently. Everything we perceive exists for us as a result of convention and labeling and is therefore dependent on many other things. Accepting this statement—realizing interdependence—simply means we realize how interrelated things fundamentally are.

The Reality We Create

We have to question our basic perception of the world as we come to understand interdependence. As we begin to live with the intention of lessening our attachments, our fears, and our aversions, we then continually remind ourselves of this perception. Truly understanding interdependence smashes the walls within our minds between "me" and "other." Recognizing we're all part of a huge and magnificent unity makes pride, jealousy, greed, and malice completely irrelevant and unnecessary. We've been focusing on inert things, but this interconnectedness applies to living beings, as well. This means others' happiness and suffering should be a serious concern for everyone. The attempt to build our happiness on others' misery isn't just amoral, it's also unrealistic.

As a central teaching of Buddhism, emptiness means that all phenomena lack "inherent existence," which is to say that no phenomenon can be a completely independent, self-sufficient, and self-enclosed entity or event; everything interconnects with everything else in a web of interpenetration. This teaching has profound consequences in our daily life, so let's spend some time to become clear about the implications.

Emptiness doesn't mean nothing exists. This is contrary to common sense and to the experience of every one of us. Additionally, the word emptiness, as we understand it in our modern culture, often has negative connotations attached to it. When we say, "I feel empty," which is a psychological state, we usually mean that we are feeling sad or depressed. People don't think of emptiness as a positive thing for which to aim. Even though Buddhist emptiness doesn't mean loneliness or separateness, it's difficult to completely forget and remove the emotional baggage tied to the word.

For those who find the term "emptiness" problematic, the word "spaciousness" often works a lot better. All of us would enjoy a little more spaciousness in our life. By implication, spaciousness implies that the nature of our everyday life is crowded in some way. This doesn't mean we have a busy life, although, of course, that can be part of the issue. Spaciousness specifically refers to our mindscape.

The First Step—Quieting the Mind

Generations of Buddhist adepts and practitioners, over thousands of years, have sat in meditation and found that, although mental states and processes often appear to be relatively static, upon close examination, all the immediate contents of the mind as well as our awareness of them are constantly in flux. Thoughts arise and pass away every second. A relatively homogenous and oppressive mental state, such as depression, may endure for seconds or even months, but that stream of emotion consists of discrete pulses of awareness, each of finite duration. There's nothing static in the human psyche, although habits may become deeply ingrained over the course of a lifetime. [18]

Our mindscape is terribly cluttered. We're like hoarders, bringing up past memories and events, hashing over what was said to us and the tone used while concurrently thinking about how cool the newest iPhone is and that we need one. On and on it goes until we fall asleep. And sometimes we're unable to sleep because of the preponderance of our unceasing mental activity.

Our consciousness apprehends and labels individual material and mental objects in our environment and crystalizes them into separate and distinct entities. We label these objects, feelings, and experiences as agreeable, disagreeable, or neutral. For an agreeable thing, we see it as good and will begin to hope and desire it, until we develop yearning thoughts. Disagreeable things, on the other hand, are seen as bad and often create aversion, anxiety, or even stronger feelings, like hatred. [19] To those things that we find agreeable, we develop attachment. To those that we find disagreeable, we develop aversion, and to those things we deem as neutral, we feel indifference.

Returning to our discussion of emptiness, or spaciousness, the degree to which we can release the constant chatter in our mind is the degree to which emptiness or spaciousness is allowed to enter our life. When I shared with you in the last chapter my experience of practicing aikido, I was talking about my growing awareness of what it means to have a mind that's settled and quiet.

As any of you who've practiced meditation know, it's not a question of willfully turning the internal dialogue off. That just doesn't work. By incorporating some of the Buddhist contemplative practices into your daily life—in particular, the practice of mindfulness—we can begin to settle the mind. As the mind begins to quiet, something truly remarkable occurs. We'll discuss this process in detail in the next chapter.

Integrating these contemplative practices into everyday life helps us shift our priorities from the mindless pursuit of mundane, moment-to-moment pleasures to the creation of genuine happiness and freedom from all mental and even some physical afflictions. Craving, hostility, and delusion all radically subside, and, as a result of our increasing insight into the profound interdependence of all beings, love and compassion spontaneously arise. [20]

The implication is that the integration of contemplative practices into our daily life allows that which has been hidden and obscured to be revealed. The "that" which is being pointed to is the recognition that our perception of ourselves as a separate, isolated self is an illusion. The understanding that everything in the universe isn't only a part of a unity but only exists because of this unity brings a deep relaxation to the psyche.

Everything is a temporal expression of a single but seamless, ever-changing landscape. Our awareness of this brings emptiness vividly into our daily life. We move beyond a mere intellectual understanding that we're all connected and we're part of the suffering of others. Our daily life gradually becomes endowed with qualities of what is termed "enlightenment"— wisdom, bliss, compassion, clarity, and courage.

The idea of observing the mind with the mind may seem problematic to many because it seems at odds with the separation of subject and object that characterizes, and is necessary for, scientific observation. This is a legitimate point. Furthermore, are we even able to observe mental states and processes with the mind? Indeed, it is. Even with no training, most of us notice our own emotional states, are able to observe thoughts and images arising in our mind, and introspectively recognize whether our minds are peaceful or anxious.

On the most basic level, we know we're conscious. We're conscious not only of objects in our environment but of our awareness of that consciousness. This faculty of perception is our only tool for observing mental phenomena. In this situation, there's no separation between the instrument of observation and the observed phenomena. This fact, however, doesn't necessarily exclude understanding the mind from the realm of scientific exploration. [21]

The Buddhist understanding of the mind challenges some of the common thoughts in the West. According to many psychologists today, even those of us with good mental health are subject to a wide range of mental distress including depression, anxiety, and various expressions of fearfulness (paranoia, etc.). The Western approach is to try to manage these mental states— when they become chronic and overwhelming—using drug therapy and counseling.

Periods of unhappiness are simply part of being human. However, in Western thought, we regard happiness as something derived from sources outside of ourselves—primarily from the acquisition of sensual pleasure via the possession of objects and other people. [21]

On the other hand, contemplatives in the Buddhist tradition state that everyone's ordinary mind is dysfunctional. It oscillates between two general states: (1) compulsive ideation (for example, what many of us experience as "falling in love") and obsessively holding onto thoughts and emotions, and (2) slipping into a stupor (which is where most of us spend our time). We're so used to experiencing this dysfunctional mind and accepting the resultant mental discomfort—believing this to be normal and reasonably healthy—that we don't consider whether this is our only option. Living with this constant sense of inner dissatisfaction, we attempt to take solace in outer pleasurable stimuli that veil our discomfort. Although the normal mind is habituated to states of attentional, emotional, and cognitive imbalances, it isn't intrinsically dysfunctional. Through the process of refining our attention and increasing our mindfulness (i.e., the practice of meditation), we're able to discover and cultivate the innate sense of well-being that emerges spontaneously from a calm and balanced mind. [21]

One of the names for the meditative practice being described here is "settling the mind in its natural state," which implies a radical deconstruction of the ways we habitually classify, evaluate, and interpret experience. As revealed in Buddhist contemplative practice, the experiential investigation of the mind involves the nature, origins, and potential of consciousness. This personal investigation is critically significant. The emphasis in this practice is on the practitioner's lived experience. Buddhism insists that the practitioner find his or her own truth in the practice, not just accept it on principle. [22]

The deepest and most reliable exploration is dependent on addressing attentional imbalances of lethargy and excitation. Without addressing these, insights won't be fully assimilated into one's life. Only when our attention is lucid, and calm can we use meditation effectively. In Buddhist thought, the qualities of luminosity and stillness are innate to the natural ground state of the mind. These qualities comprise the true and foundational "nature of mind" in Buddhist thinking. The primary challenge of this training is to settle the attention so the mind rests in that ground state. [23]

Buddhist contemplatives who've been able to abide in this authentic nature of mind, this stratum of consciousness, have discovered that they are imbued with an innate quality of bliss. In other words, when our mind settles into a deep state of equilibrium—temporarily free of lethargy, wandering, and excitation—we spontaneously experience a sense of inner peace and well-being.

A prerequisite to arriving at this substrate of consciousness is cultivating a wholesome way of life that supports both internal mental balance and also harmonious relationships. This is the essence of Buddhist ethics, which is the foundation of all Buddhist practice. [21] The keys to this ethical life are described in detail in the fourth of the Buddhist teachings known as The Four Noble Truths. Let's begin with an overview of these Four Noble Truths.

The Four Noble Truths

The articulation of the concept of emptiness within the philosophical vehicle of Buddhism is clear and precise. The explication of emptiness is developed through an exact and profound analysis of how our perception functions in relation to what is defined as ultimate reality. As this analysis progresses, so also does our view of reality. The unveiling of illusion proceeds from one point of view to another through increasingly subtle phases. [24]

The framework that supports this investigative analysis is the Four Noble Truths, which are described as: suffering exists, the source of suffering, the cessation of suffering together with its source, and the path which leads to its cessation. More formally, these truths are rendered:

The First Noble Truth – The truth of suffering

The Second Noble Truth – The truth of the cause of suffering

The Third Noble Truth – The truth of the end of suffering

The Fourth Noble Truth – The truth of the path that frees us from suffering

While Buddhist contemplatives place primary emphasis on fathoming the true nature of mind, their orientation in this endeavor has been fundamentally pragmatic. The first task is to recognize the nature and full range of suffering to which humans are vulnerable. This is the insight addressed by the First Noble Truth. The Second Noble Truth posits that the essential causes of suffering are found within the mind—specifically, in the form of cognitive, emotional, and attentional imbalances. The Third Noble truth hypothesizes that it's possible for these afflictions to be irreversibly dispelled. The Fourth Noble Truth presents detailed practices for observing our mental processes and experimenting with techniques for transforming the mind to enhance inner calm and bliss. [24]

A common rendering of the Four Noble Truths tells us that life is suffering, suffering is caused by craving and attachment, suffering ends when we stop craving and release our attachments, and the way to do this is to live a righteous life in body, speech, and mind. This righteous and joyful life can be achieved by following what is known as the Eightfold Path, which I'll discuss a little bit more at the end of this chapter.

Quite often, people get hung up on the "life is suffering" part and decide Buddhism isn't for them. They don't want to acknowledge this truth much less explore it in their own life. If this phrase causes a problem for you, try substituting "life is unsatisfactory" or "life is stressful." Surely, we can all agree that, at times, our lives are stressful, and this stress causes us suffering.

We're exposed to almost constant messages about what's of value and what we need to accomplish, buy, or experience to make us happy. Much of this marketing—in addition to not leading us to genuine happiness—is more insidiously powerful than we realize. This ever-present environment of advertising that attempts to manipulate our values and desires has created a culture that leaves us feeling chronically unsatisfied.

However, if you take the time to appreciate what the Four Noble Truths are really about, you'll see they're based on your own common sense and experience. We suffer. That's a fact of life. Some of us suffer much more than others, but we all experience disappointment, heartbreak, resentment, and regret. However, these Truths don't just point out why we experience life as suffering and leave us in our misery. They clarify the nature of suffering in a logical way and provide a logical way to move out of that suffering. Let's look at them one at a time.

The First Noble Truth: Life is Suffering

In Buddhism, a core insight is that what gets us into trouble are the ways we typically view our world and our blind clinging to these ways of seeing. At the root of our suffering—i.e., primary to engendering, perpetuating, and exacerbating it—are our habitual (mis)perceptions and the illusions and delusions that this incorrect way of seeing creates.

Of course, everyone's life, even the Dalai Lama's, contains some suffering, at least at times—pain (emotional and physical), disease, disappointment, frustration, even anger. This is what the First Noble Truth acknowledges—the existence of suffering.

When we begin to inquire into how this suffering comes about, we see there are many seemingly external causes, but, in fact, it isn't what happens *to* us but how we *react* to what happens to us that's the source of suffering. When we're able to recognize unhelpful habitual patterns of thought, speech, and action, we begin to see how these result in the contraction of our compassion. This contraction is the main source of our suffering.

The Second Noble Truth: The Origin of Suffering

The Second Noble Truth teaches that the cause of suffering is greed or desire. This can also be construed as wishing things were different than they are. The actual word for suffering in Sanskrit, *dukkha,* is more accurately translated as "thirst" or "craving."

We continually search for something outside ourselves to make us happy. But no matter how successful we are in obtaining these objects of desire, we're never satisfied. The craving continues. The Second Noble Truth isn't saying that we must give up everything we love to find happiness. The real issue here is more subtle—it's our *attachment* to the outcome of our desire, and our aversion to releasing our desire that gets us into trouble.

The Buddha taught that this thirst or craving is based on ignorance of our true self. Some people go through life grabbing one thing after another in an attempt to feel a sense of security. Others accumulate money, objects, or other people to try to make themselves feel more worthy. We attach ourselves not only to physical things but also to ideas and opinions about ourselves and the world around us. Then we grow frustrated when the world doesn't behave the way we think it should and our lives don't conform to our expectations.

The psychological reasons behind this craving are many, but the foundational explanation is the same for all of us—a misunderstanding of our true nature.

Embarking on a meditation practice is a terrific way to bring about a radical change in our perspective. Once we see the truth of our nature—and of the nature of the everything—the tendency to divide the universe into "me" and "everything else" fades away. We see that our happiness isn't found "out there." In time, the practitioner is better able to enjoy life's experiences without judgment, bias, feeling a need to manipulate to achieve a certain outcome, or any of the other mental activities we constantly engage in to try to make the world conform to our wishes.

The Third Noble Truth: The Cessation of Suffering

To end our suffering, we must stop this mindless pursuing and clinging. But how do we do that? The fact is, this can't be accomplished by an act of will. It's impossible to just vow to yourself, "Okay, from now on I won't crave anything." This doesn't work because the conditions that give rise to craving are still present.

The Second Noble Truth tells us that we cling to things we believe will make us happy or keep us safe. Grasping for one object, idea, or person after another never satisfies us for long because it's all impermanent—in the sense that everything and everybody changes all the time, including ourselves and our desires. It's only when we see this for ourselves that we can stop grasping. Every time we see this and acknowledge it, the letting go becomes easier. Once we realize that obtaining objects of desire has never made us happy and never will, the craving begins to disappear of its own accord.

Learning to quiet the mind helps us to discern what we truly need in any given moment. Many times (maybe even most times) nothing is needed. We realize, in the moment, we're OK.

All the pain we thought we were in was being caused by worrying about something that may never happen or revisiting something in the past that made us feel bad. Relaxing the mind and experiencing the "now" allows space for those spontaneous realizations to emerge. We begin to have epiphanies—such as, "Instead of doing office work tonight, I'm going to hang out with my kid." We begin to live more and more in the moment—seeing it, appreciating it, not feeling a need to change it, and expanding our sense of well-being by recognizing our blessed place in the universe.

The Fourth Noble Truth: The Eightfold Path to End Suffering

The Fourth Noble Truth is a path describing eight broad areas of practice that touch every part of our lives. The Eightfold Path addresses everything from ethical conduct to what you do for a living, and emphasizes moment-to-moment mindfulness. Every action of body, speech, and mind is addressed by this path. It's a path of exploration and discipline we walk for the rest of our life, and, with each step, we come closer to joy.

The Eightfold Path consists of eight practices: right view, right resolve, right speech, right conduct, right livelihood, right effort, right mindfulness, and right "*samadhi*" (meditative absorption or union). Without the Eightfold Path, the first three Noble Truths would just be a theory; something for philosophers to argue about. The practice of the Eightfold Path brings order into our life and allows us to bloom. [25]

In the next chapters, we'll explore a mindfulness practice you can do at home. This exercise consists of a meditative practice and internal dialogues to help dismantle repetitive thought patterns. This is a simple practice, so if you've never done meditation or don't even know what it is exactly, don't worry. As I said at the beginning of the book, this practice takes about 20 minutes of your day, and anyone can do it. What you'll receive in return is better health, enhanced creativity, more passion, and a directed, mindful life.

Some Closing Thoughts

The merging of the quantum and Buddhist views we've discussed in this chapter has profound implications for you as well as for the world at large. My very existence requires your existence. There's no such thing as isolated or independent existence, whether we're speaking of particles or people. We aren't autonomous, self-existing individuals. We're expressions of our mutual connectedness to each other, the community, and the larger environment. It follows, then, that if you suffer, I suffer. [26] Indeed, in both the Buddhist and quantum views of the world, if any being, no matter how small, suffers, the entire universe suffers. This isn't just a poetic statement. We need only look at the news to see how, when one species of tiny creature goes extinct—often a species we never even knew existed—it has repercussions throughout the planet. We deny this interconnectedness at our peril.

A word about Buddhism and its teachings – it's important to understand that Buddhism isn't a religion. The teachings of Buddha are meant as a guide for understanding ourselves and our environment, and, as such, Buddhism isn't at odds with any religion. I personally know Jews and Catholics who practice Buddhism and not only feel no conflict but find that Buddhism clarifies and enriches their spiritual tradition. These meditative practices don't distract from their faith but, in fact, enhance it. The concept of God isn't a discussion in the Buddhist philosophical framework. This doesn't mean that God is denied; it's just that the teachings are focused on how we create suffering for ourselves and the path for achieving direct, experiential insight into the interdependent nature of reality. Certainly, a belief in God may give us a feeling of closeness with our Creator and encourage us to become more loving and altruistic as an expression of our gratitude in knowing God.

What's emphasized in the Buddhist teachings is living an ethical life, which yields genuine happiness while engendering deep compassion for all beings. To quote the Japanese poet Ikkyu (1394-1491):

> *"Many paths lead from*
>
> *The foot of the mountain*
>
> *But at the peak*
>
> *We all gaze at the*
>
> *Single bright moon."*

Let me leave you with these words of the Dalai Lama: "When embarking upon a spiritual path, it is important that you engage in a practice that is most suited to your mental development, your dispositions, and your spiritual inclinations…Through this, one can bring about inner transformation, the inner tranquility that will make that individual spiritually mature and a warm hearted, whole, and good and kind person. That is the consideration one must use in seeking spiritual nourishment." [27]

References:

1. Ricard, Matthieu. The Quantum and the Lotus: A Journey to the Frontiers Where Science and Buddhism Meet (pp. 11). Crown/Archetype. Kindle Edition.
2. Graham Smetham. Quantum Buddhism : Dancing In Emptiness - Reality Revealed at the Interface of Quantum Physics & Buddhist Philosophy (Kindle Location 5222). Lulu.com. Kindle Edition
3. Ibid., Kindle Location 2411.
4. Merali, Z. Solving Biology's Mysteries Using Quantum Mechanics, Discover Magazine, Dec. 2014
5. Graham Smetham, ibid., Kindle Location 5738.
6. https://en.wikipedia.org/wiki/Wave_function
7. Graham Smetham, ibid. Kindle Location 5457.
8. Ibid., Kindle Location 5468.
9. Rosenblum, Bruce. Quantum Physics of Consciousness (Kindle Locations 412-416). Cosmology Science Publishers. Kindle Edition.
10. Wallace, B. A. (2002). A Science of Consciousness. The Pacific World: Journal of the Institute of Buddhist Studies, (No. 4), 15–32.
11. Vedral, Vlatko. Decoding Reality: The Universe as Quantum Information (Oxford Landmark Science) (p. 199). OUP Oxford. Kindle Edition.
12. Smetham, Graham "Quantum Emptiness: The Quantum Illusion-like Nature of Reality" Many Roads. https://bodhicharya.org, Feb. 2011.
13. Graham Smetham, Quantum Buddhism : Dancing In Emptiness - Reality Revealed at the Interface of Quantum Physics & Buddhist Philosophy, Kindle Locations 46-48).
14. Schrödinger, E. The Physical Aspect of the Living Cell, (1944), Based on lectures delivered under the auspices of the Dublin Institute for Advanced Studies at Trinity College, Dublin, in February 1943.

15. Vedral, Vlatko, ibid., pp. 200-201.
16. Graham Smetham. Quantum Buddhism : Dancing In Emptiness - Reality Revealed at the Interface of Quantum Physics & Buddhist Philosophy (Kindle Location 1371). Lulu.com. Kindle Edition.
17. https://en.wikipedia.org/wiki/Homunculus_argument
18. Wallace, B. Alan. Hidden Dimensions: The Unification of Physics and Consciousness (Columbia Series in Science and Religion) (p. 44). Columbia University Press. Kindle Edition.
19. Ibid., p. 112.
20. Ibid, p. 99.
21. Wallace, B. A. (2002). A Science of Consciousness. The Pacific World: Journal of the Institute of Buddhist Studies, (No. 4), 15–32.
22. Wallace, B. Alan. Stilling the Mind: Shamatha Teachings from Dudjom Lingpa's Vajra Essence (p. 67). Wisdom Publications. Kindle Edition.
23. Wallace, B. Alan. Stilling the Mind: Shamatha Teachings from Dudjom Lingpa's Vajra Essence (p. 111). Wisdom Publications. Kindle Edition.
24. Graham Smetham, ibid., Kindle Location 951).
25. Burbea, Rob. Seeing That Frees: Meditations on Emptiness and Dependent Arising (Kindle Locations 210-215). Hermes Amāra. Kindle Edition
26. Mansfield, Vic. Tibetan Buddhism and Modern Physics: Toward a Union of Love and Knowledge (p. 91). Templeton Press. Kindle Edition.
27. Dalai Lama, The Good Heart: A Buddhist Perspective on the Teachings of Jesus (Boston: Wisdom Publications, 1996), p. 73.

Chapter 7
The Practice

"Practice is realization and realization is practice"

- Dogen Zenji

We've discussed the theory that consciousness permeates all that we know and isn't separate from ourselves. Consciousness is energy, which quantum-field theory has defined as a probabilities wave function. The collapse of that wave function creates our perceptions, thoughts, emotions, and sensations.

Further, we've learned that Buddhism has, over the last 2500 hundred years, actively studied consciousness and mapped out clearly defined states that the mind is able to experience to reveal this undivided sea of consciousness. Theories and scientific research in quantum physics coupled with Buddhist insights into contemplative meditation form the groundwork for attempting to explain how brain waves initiate transactions in the natural world—how our thoughts interact with everything and cause matter to manifest in our lives. The more we look into this phenomenon, the clearer the connection becomes. If thoughts equal energy and energy equals matter, this means our thoughts become matter. Observing our thoughts is an excellent approach for closely examining what we're creating in our life and identifying what we want to change.

Observing Our Thoughts to Discover What We're Creating

In this chapter, we investigate a practice for observing our thoughts as they manifest. By observing our thoughts, we begin to "see" what we're creating. Some of these thoughts and patterns aren't supportive in helping us to have a creative, healthy, and long life. As part of this practice, we'll explore ways to gently deconstruct thought forms that reinforce our belief that we're separate from the sea of consciousness in which we exist.

The increasing body of scientific research supports the possibility of dismantling our habituated thoughts by mindfulness-based meditation practices. These practices also reduce stress, which has been demonstrated in the growing evidence of meditation's beneficial effects on psychological, neurological, endocrine, and immune variables. [1]

Chronic, low-grade inflammation is associated with many of the most common causes of morbidity and mortality around the world including cardiovascular and metabolic disease, cancer, and neuropsychiatric disorders. Research suggests that mindfulness-based behavioral interventions may produce beneficial effects in individuals who have chronic diseases where chronic inflammation is a significant contributing factor. Data presented in recent studies support the hypothesis that mindfulness-based meditation practice affects some of the biological mechanisms that are targeted by anti-inflammatory drugs such as histone deacetylase inhibitors (HDACi) or cyclooxygenase (COX) inhibitors. [2]

More and more, the practice of meditation is associated with successes in pain management. [3] One theory is that mechanisms such as enhanced emotional and cognitive control alter the perception of pain in people who meditate on a regular basis. Findings suggest that peripheral anti-inflammatory and analgesic molecular mediators play a role in the regulation of pain initiation and maintenance, and they also respond to meditation. Meditation-based practices may inhibit the pro-inflammatory NF (nuclear factor)-kappa B pathway in blood cells, which is a reproducible molecular outcome. Practitioners studied include those engaging in the relaxation response [4] and caregivers of family members with dementia who practice yogic meditation. [5,6]

The Approach

The approach to meditation practice is simple and direct, and the results are profound. We begin by settling or quieting the mind. We make a commitment of 20 minutes a day to sit in silent meditation. All that's required is a willingness to explore uncomfortable and difficult stuff that may arise. I'll provide you with the means to dialogue with this stuff, which will result in its becoming less painful and, eventually, releasing its effect on your life.

I use the term "stuff" in a playful manner because we always have stuff coming up. The purpose of meditation is for us to get into the nitty gritty when we look at our stuff. As our practice begins to stabilize, we realize that absolutely everything that arises in our minds is "grist for the mill" and enhances our awareness of who we truly are.

Here's a vignette from my life that illustrates what I mean by studying our mind at the granular level:

I like to take early morning walks in my neighborhood. The air is cool, I see people out walking their dogs, and there isn't much traffic. One morning, I was walking and saw a fellow approaching who I didn't know. As we passed one another, I made eye contact and smiled. He didn't respond—no head nod, no hand wave, no smile, no nothing.

A couple of days later, I was out walking again, and the same guy came walking toward me. As we passed this time, I noticed I had the thought that I wasn't going to respond in any way to him. I didn't, and we walked past each other with no acknowledgment. I took four or five more steps, and another thought emerged: *What was all that about, Warren?* Why would I make a decision to inhibit my spontaneity?

We'll discuss this kind of mental inquiry in the next chapter. The point is, meditation is about being aware of and investigating our thoughts and feelings without judgment. It's self-research approached from a place of open curiosity.

Perhaps the most important insight we can have is to realize that behind every experience of suffering lies resistance. This manifests in the form of resisting being thwarted in obtaining what we want or resisting what's happening to us that we don't want.

Making a Commitment to Ourselves That Will Lead to a Happier, Healthier Life

The commitment you make to practice is a commitment to yourself—not from a place of 'you must do this because it's supposed to be good for you' but from a place of compassion for yourself. Such compassion recognizes an internal longing for greater understanding of yourself and a desire to engage more fully in life, or the commitment could be inspired by a deep understanding of the Four Noble Truths. We recognize we suffer or have stress in our life, and we want to explore the nature of that suffering in order to relieve ourselves of it.

The approach that we're embarking on—meditation—is part of the Eightfold Path. The process is one of inquiry to examine the causes of our suffering. The vignette I shared with you is an example of this inquiry in which I observed my thoughts and reactions in a particular situation. This would be considered an open-eye meditation and, in my case, a walking open-eye meditation. Whether the eyes are open or closed, meditation implies that there's some degree of settledness in the mind that allows such inquiry. In later chapters, we'll talk more about bringing the clarity of a meditative state into our everyday life.

One of the goals of meditation is for us to see that our mind has concocted an illusion (or many illusions), and we've fallen for it. Even if it's too late to correct our thoughts or behavior in a particular situation, recognizing our illusory view of that situation is important. We gain insight into the fabrication and essential emptiness of everything we perceive.

Our individual perspectives are discussed in the upcoming chapter, and it's important to understand how they can be destructive in our life depending on the degree of rigidity to which we hold onto them. As we continue to practice, we see more clearly that we naturally move among states of greater calm, spaciousness, kindness, and equanimity on the one hand and states of relatively less calm and more agitation on the other, all the time. We're gradually able to see the tendency of our mind to become caught in grosser fabrications when we're in states of craving, reactivity, and confusion. With practice, we can recognize when this is occurring sooner and, eventually, choose to step out of it.

Fundamentally, what gets us into trouble are the ways we typically view things and our blind clinging to these ways of seeing. At the root of our suffering—and what's responsible for perpetuating and exacerbating it—are our habitual concepts and the perceptions they spawn. [7]

Cultivating Spaciousness

As we travel this meditative journey, we'll find that, the more we experience a settled mind, the more that loving kindness, compassion, generosity, and deep care for the world open naturally as a consequence. Settling the mind opens us to love because, as we discussed in the quantum chapters, the meditative experience brings us in direct contact with the inter-relatedness of all phenomena. This meditative space is one of emptiness (or, if you prefer "spaciousness").

Our investigation is simply into how the mind gives solidity to experience and fabricates suffering through the very ways we relate to and perceive things. We'll learn to untangle the knots of stress and suffering. As happens with all deliberate shifts in our way of perceiving, the more we meditate, the more accessible this equanimity becomes. The more we practice inclining the mind to notice spaciousness, the easier it becomes to actually dwell in this freedom of spaciousness and experience a life that's richer and more nurturing.

In any moment, if we don't have a certain amount of mindfulness, there can be a tendency for our attention to get dragged into the associations, reactivity, and stories that a stimulus (anything we experience with our senses, remember, or think) might trigger in us. That term, "mindfulness," in this context, means "aware presence." This refers to us having (some) awareness of our actions and thoughts in the moment rather than being engrossed in internal stories, emotions, or reactivity. Those may be going on, but we have a degree of mindfulness that lets us know they're occurring.

Pharmakon, in philosophy and critical thinking, is a term that refers to a composite of three meanings: remedy, poison, and scapegoat. [8] In today's culture, mindfulness is often used as a pharmakon for a heterogeneous array of modern infirmities. There are a number of current publications relating to this understanding of mindfulness. These include *Mindful Work, The Mindful Way Through Depression, Mindful Birthing, Mindful Movements, The Mindful Child, The Mindful Teen, Mindful Eating,* and *The Mindful Way Through Stress.* In these books, mindfulness has come to represent a dizzying range of meanings in an attempt to appeal to popular audiences. [9]

Although it can be useful to think of mindfulness as 'being with things as they really are," it's more accurate—and more helpful for our purposes—to understand basic mindfulness practice as a way of looking that merely results in us fabricating a little less than we normally do. When we become aware of our stories and the proliferation of internal chatter and pay attention in a closer, simpler, and more continuous way to aspects of our experience, we're able to see through a certain level of abstraction and fabrication. As a result, we don't engage in perceptions and processes of the mind that cause us to fabricate quite so much. [10]

I'll continue to use the term mindfulness in the remaining chapters, and I want to be scrupulous in its meaning. It's vital that we create space between ourselves and our stories and internal chatter. However, we must understand that the Second and Third Noble Truths aren't avoided by mindfulness practice. This isn't about escaping suffering but facing and overcoming it.

Creating the Environment

Here are some pointers to consider when setting up your meditation space. If you've meditated before, you'll be aware of most of this, and if you already have a style of meditation you're comfortable with, continue with that.

When you're just starting a meditation practice, it's important to have a comfortable, quiet environment for your practice. Choose a private space where you won't be disturbed. If you don't have such a space, you can create one by posting a note on the door of your bedroom or office or telling the people around you that you'll be meditating for the next twenty minutes or so. If there's a phone in your room, unplug it, and be sure to turn off the ringer or buzzer on your cell phone.

If practical, wear comfortable clothes and adjust the temperature in the room so you won't be too cool or too warm. It's also good to have a timer or alarm clock set for the period of your mediation so you don't need to think about the time. There are free meditation-timing apps that can be downloaded onto your laptop, tablet, or cell phone. They have a pleasant-sounding chime or bell to end the meditation.

Here's one I like: http://www.onlinemeditationtimer.com/.

You can sit on a chair, couch, or meditation cushion on the floor. You can even lie on your back if you prefer, as long as there's no risk you'll fall asleep. The only requirement is that you stay in place for the duration of your meditation. You don't need to be immobile, but it's advised that you sit with your spine straight and your body relaxed. If you're uncomfortable, you can move your body slightly if you wish. Just don't get up and move around. Remain comfortable, quiet, and awake. You can leave your eyes open, close them, or have your eyelids at "half-mast" in a relaxed fashion.

If you're new to meditation or would like assistance in settling your mind, check out Appendix 1 for resources that can help.

The Purpose of Meditation

You've set up a space for your meditation, so what are you doing as you sit quietly? There are a number of possible ways to meditate. Some meditation teachers teach their students to follow the breath by visualizing the rise and fall of the abdomen. Others recommend focusing attention on the sensation of how the body is positioned by noticing how your body is sitting on the cushion, how your hands touch one another, or the feeling of one leg against the other.

The method I'll explain here involves following your breath. Before we go on to specific instructions, let's examine the reason behind this method. You may be wondering, why choose a focus of attention? We are, after all, trying to develop awareness. Why can't we just sit down and be aware of whatever is present in our mind? There are, in fact, meditation practices that do this. They're sometimes referred to as non-dual meditation. In the next chapter, we'll investigate this approach as a method of inquiry.

First and foremost, you need to begin to settle your mind. Thought is an inherently complicated process, and the mind is tricky. It's easy to get tangled in our chain of thoughts. One thought leads to another, which leads to another, and another, and another, and so on. Fifteen minutes go by, and we suddenly realize we spent our whole meditation time stuck in a daydream or a knot of worries.

Being aware of a thought and thinking a thought are two different things. That difference is subtle and is primarily one of feeling. A thought you're aware of in a meditative state feels light, and there's a sense of distance between that thought and your awareness of it. The thought arises lightly, like a bubble. Then it floats away without dragging you into a thought chain.

A thought that hijacks our attention feels much heavier. It's ponderous, commanding, and compulsive. It grabs control of your mind and sucks you away from the rest of your thoughts. These are obsessional thoughts and will lead straight to the next thought in the chain—apparently with no gap between them.

This type of thought, which colonizes your attention, causes a similar tension throughout the body, with contracting muscles or a faster heartbeat. There's a clear difference between awareness of a thought and actively thinking a thought, but meditative concentration allows us to see this difference. In addition, mindful observation of our thoughts and feelings reveals that any craving or clinging is always accompanied by and reflected in blocks and knots in the body.

Meditation affects our mind by calming the thought process and sharpening our awareness of what's happening in our mind. This results in an improved ability to examine our thoughts and our reactions to them. We use meditation as a microscope for viewing subtle mental and physical states and how they change. We're able to achieve one-pointedness (focus) of mind through calm and consistent attention. Without this detached reference point of ourselves as observers, we get lost, overcome by the ceaseless waves of changing thoughts flowing round and round in our mind.

"Watching our breath" acts as that vital reference point. Of course, we can't actually watch our breath, but this phrase means focusing our awareness on a sensation of the breathing process, which I'll describe shortly. We're unaware of distraction unless we have a central focus to be distracted from. Watching the breath is the frame of reference against which we can view the incessant changes that characterize normal thinking. When the mind wanders, we draw it back by focusing on the breath.

Meditation Tames the Mind

Meditation tames the mind, and being aware of your posture will help with this taming process. Once you're in a quiet space where you won't be interrupted and are sitting comfortably in a chair or on a meditation cushion, make sure you're as upright as possible and your spine is straight but not rigid. Your chin should be level with the floor—not uplifted or dropped toward your chest. As we continue sitting, our chest may collapse a little around the sternum. This has the effect of reducing the air volume within the lungs, and this reduced air volume may bring on a sense of drowsiness that may result in you falling asleep. Check your posture from time to time and gently straighten the spine if necessary. If your chin drops, this also restricts air flow and causes drowsiness. Gently lifting the head and straightening the spine allows aware presence to permeate your meditation.

Within these parameters, become aware of your breathing. When thoughts arise, don't cling to them but return to watching your breath. Do this every time thoughts or feelings arise. With regard to thoughts and feelings, a good mantra is, "Let it come, let it go, let it be." There's no right or wrong way to meditate but focusing on the breath is a good way to calmly explore your mental landscape.

Don't follow your thoughts and don't try to figure anything out or analyze your feelings. There's nothing you need to do except breathe and be aware of your breathing. If you become captivated by a particular line of thought, a feeling, or a physical sensation, as soon as you notice this has happened, gently return to your breathing. There's nothing to correct or adjust, no guidelines about what you're supposed to do except to notice what's going on in your head without reacting to it or engaging it. Thoughts, feelings, and sensations will continuously emerge, and, when they do, gently return to your breathing.

Why is the Breath Used as the Meditation Object?

You may be wondering why the breath is used as the meditation object. When meditating, you want the object of meditation to be one that promotes presence and awareness. It should be easily available. Breathing satisfies these criteria and more. Every human being needs to breathe. Breathing is necessary, and we bring it with us everywhere we go. It's constantly accessible, and never ends from birth until death.

Breathing can be done without directly thinking about it. Furthermore, like all aspects of life, it's a process of constant change. The cycle of breath going in and out represents the rhythm and change of life.

Many of the sensations of breathing are subtle, yet they become quite distinct when you learn to tune into them. This takes some effort and work, but anybody can do it. Breathing itself isn't difficult, and the work to focus on it isn't too taxing. For all these reasons, the breath makes an ideal object of meditation. Normally, breathing is an involuntary process, and its pace depends more on our physical activity and emotional state than the involvement of our will. However, we can, by using our attention, change our breath to slow it down or speed it up, make it long and smooth or short and choppy.

Because breathing is common to all living things, an experiential understanding of the breathing process brings us closer to other beings and demonstrates our inherent interconnectedness with all of life. Finally, breathing is a present-time process, occurring right now. Living in the present isn't something we normally do. So much of our time is spent thinking about memories, wanting to relive or change the past, or planning for the future, making plans and getting caught up in worries. Watching the breath puts us smack-dab in the here-and-now.

By observing the breath, we are completely brought to the present. We're pulled out of the swamp of our own memories, worries, and plans and brought into the full experience of now. In this way, our breath gives us a living slice of reality. Mindfully considering this miniature model of life brings us to insights that can be applied to our own experience of life.

Finding the Breath

To use the breath as an object of meditation, we first have to find it. What you're looking for is the physical, tactile sensation of the air that passes in and out of the nostrils. You may be able to best sense it at the tip of the nose, but the ideal spot varies from person to person, depending on the shape of the nose and one's ability to perceive the subtleties of air moving in and out of the nostrils. To find your own point, take a quick deep breath through your nose and see if you can sense air moving in the nasal area just inside the nostrils or on the area above your upper lip. Now exhale and notice where you feel the flow of air. This will be the focus when you put your attention on your breath. Once you've clearly located this point, don't deviate from that spot. This single point of focus will keep your attention fixed.

With this point in mind, you track your breathing with clear but relaxed attention. Focus on your breath and how it naturally enters and leaves your body. For now, don't change the breath, just allow it to move naturally. Beginners often have trouble with this and want to regulate or emphasize their breath. To make it easier to focus on their sensation, they unconsciously accentuate their breathing, but the effect is a forced, unnatural effort that actually makes it more difficult to concentrate. Let go and allow the process to continue at its own pace.

It may sound easy, but this is trickier than expected. If your will is getting in the way, don't be discouraged. Once you observe it, you can use it as an opportunity to recognize the nature of conscious intention. Notice the delicate nature of the interrelationship between your breath and the impulses to both control and cease control of your breath. It may feel frustrating while working on this, but it is an invaluable learning experience. Also, it's a passing phase. Eventually, your breathing will easily move at its own rhythm, and you won't consciously or unconsciously try to manipulate it.

Breathing, which might seem mundane and boring, is actually an incredibly complex and fascinating phenomenon. It's composed of slight variations. There are inhalation and exhalation, long breath and short breath, deep breath, shallow breath, smooth breath, and ragged breath. There are gasps and sighs and "catches" of the breath. These categories combine with one another in subtle and intricate ways.

Observe your breath closely. Really study it. You'll find enormous variations as well as repeated patterns. It's like a symphony. Don't observe just the bare outline of when you inhale and exhale. There's more to pay attention to here than just in-breath and out-breath. Your breathing changes with your emotions, your thoughts, and what you hear and see, and you may come to find how the depth and speed of your breath alters with these things.

Simply note these alterations in your breathing when they occur, and return your attention to observing the sensations of breathing. Every time you're distracted, bring your focus back to your breath again, and again, and again. Eventually, your distractions become fewer because your ability to maintain a meditative state becomes stronger.

Dealing with Distractions

When you first begin your practice, don't be surprised if you have some trouble. Your mind will likely wander frantically jumping on wild tangents. Try not to worry. This agitated-mind phenomenon is well known, and every advanced meditator has had to deal with this when they began. They've worked through it, and you can, too. Anytime it happens, just take note that your mind has wandered into daydreaming, planning, worrying, or whatever the case may be. Don't get upset with yourself. Instead gently return to your focus on the physical sensation of the breath. Do this every time you notice your mind has wandered—which, for a while, will be again and again and again.

Meditation is an active function. Focusing on your breath places strong, energetic attention on one point. As you sit, notice your sense of awareness, which is often experienced as a bright, clean alertness. Notice the tactile feeling of the in-breath. Observe the touch sensation of the out-breath. Breathe in, breathe out, and watch what happens. When you've been doing this for some time—weeks or months—you'll begin to sense breathing as a physical touch.

With practice, your concentration will deepen, and your mind won't jump from thought to thought so often. Your breathing will slow, and you'll be able to track it more and more consistently, with fewer mental interruptions. You'll become aware of experiencing a state of great calm. Agitation goes away. Fear flees. These are beautiful, clear, blissful states of mind. They're temporary and often end when your meditation ends, yet the afterglow of such a sense of well-being lingers and begins to change your life.

At the end of a meditation session, it's not unusual to feel refreshed in both mind and body. You feel filled with peaceful, buoyant, joyous energy that you can take into your daily life. The purpose of meditation isn't to solve your problems, even though having some quiet time may seem like an ideal opportunity to do that. You may notice your thoughts returning to those problem during the session, which ends up sidetracking the real purpose—to focus on your breathing. Don't think about your worries and concerns while meditating. Gently push them aside. Meditation is the time to take a break from the constant busyness and worries surrounding you. Think of mediation as a vacation. Trust yourself, and trust your ability to handle those problems and other issues later using the clarity and freshness of mind created during your meditation. Trust yourself, and you'll see this will actually happen.

There will be times when you forget to meditate, or you fall asleep while meditating. There will be times you become lost in deep thought...often for great stretches of time. When you notice your mind is far away from your intended purpose, just inhale and resume watching the breath. Don't be frustrated and give up. Remember, there's no such thing as a bad meditation. Even if your mind wanders through most of your session, the discipline is still beneficial, so stick with it. Refresh your resolve with every cycle of breath, and, in this way, you build your practice. Observe each breath with care and precision, one split-second at a time. Unbroken awareness will eventually result.

Mindfulness of your breathing is an exercise in present-time awareness. When done properly, you'll only be aware of what's going on in that present moment. You don't remember what has happened and you don't look toward the future. You forget about the last breath, and you don't anticipate the next one. With the beginning of a breath, you don't skip forward to the end of that inhalation, and you don't look toward the upcoming exhalation. You simply stay with what is actually taking place right then. Once your inhalation begins, that's what you focus on—that and nothing else.

Meditation is a process that retrains the mind. Your goal is reaching a state in which you're completely aware of everything that's happening in your own perceived universe, exactly as and when it happens—total, unbroken awareness of the present moment. Achieving this one-pointed awareness takes practice, so we begin with small steps. We start by becoming fully aware of just one tiny increment of time, one single inhalation. And, step by step, meditation session by meditation session, your life is changed to one of more awareness at all times.

I begin each meditation session with a wish for all sentient beings to let go of the illusion of the separate, isolated self. This sets the tone and intention for my practice, and makes it about more than just me. This wish emerges from a place of deep compassion for all suffering beings—including ourselves—that resides within all of us.

Obstacles That Arise in Meditation

The meditation approach we're describing here is one of observation and acceptance. It isn't based on the premise that we need to change in order to achieve real fulfillment or on an assumption that something is missing in our life.

If you're an experienced meditator, you're already aware that obstacles arise in meditation. If meditation was easy, everyone would be doing it, right? If you're new to practice, the obstacles you should be aware of start even before you sit down— "I'm too busy," "I'm too tired," or "I'm too upset," are a few of the many variations we tell ourselves that keep us from sitting down and getting to it.

It's important not to be judgmental about yourself when obstacles arise, because they certainly will. When you find yourself avoiding your meditation practice, do this: from a place of open inquiry (meaning you're not judging your reluctance or decision not to practice), explore that reluctance or decision. Maybe the time you've selected for your practice isn't ideal. Maybe you really are tired, and a nap is what you need. Maybe you're not ready to commit to take the time necessary for practice.

It's important to learn not to take these obstacles personally and to let go of any self-criticism we might tend to attach to our investigation of them. Perceived obstacles are a normal part of the practice, but it's important to investigate their nature so we can figure out how to overcome them.

When we're deeply identified with our conditioned way of being—our beliefs, values, preferences, and their related emotions—it's not unusual for us to find some initial difficulty in settling our mind. Common psychological phenomena that hinder access to our sense of being an aware presence include:

• Attachment to suffering (because we use our suffering to create our identity)

• The habitual need to be doing something (which is programmed into us by our culture)

• The need to know what's happening to make sure we're not wasting our time

• The need to create meaning (if we can't see how meditation is benefitting us, we may feel like giving up)

• Fearful projections about unconditioned awareness (anxiety about thoughts and feelings that may arise if our mind isn't distracted)

• The tendency to make aware presence into something special rather than a natural way of perceiving our world

The Five Hindrances

Once you've made it past any initial resistance to getting into your practice, the next challenge is resistance that may arise as you're sitting. Over the course of the 2500 years in which Buddhist meditation has been practiced, the primary obstacles to practice have been clearly identified. In Buddhist terminology, they're referred to as the five hindrances. The five hindrances are: sense desire, ill-will or aversion, dullness and drowsiness, restlessness and worry, and doubt. These obstacles shouldn't be viewed as unfortunate problems. Rather, they're opportunities to develop and strengthen your practice for more mindfulness, concentration, understanding, and non-clinging.

Let me comment on each of these hindrances so you'll have a sense of the landscape when one of them arises.

• Sense desire – Hopefully this one is fairly clear. A craving for food and physical intimacy are ones that arise often. You're sitting and breathing, and you start thinking about an upcoming or past intimate encounter or one of your favorite dishes that you're going to make for dinner. Before you know it, you're lost in fantasizing about these sense desires.

• Ill-will or aversion – Feelings of ill-will or aversion arise when someone hurts you or something happens to you that feels unjust. The result is you feel ill-will and aversion toward the person or situation. Ill-will and aversion are based in fear.

• Dullness and drowsiness – These are big ones, and I'll say more about them shortly. Basically, what happens is you're sitting, you start to feel drowsy, your mind begins to drift, and then, clunk, you're asleep.

• Restlessness and worry – Mental restlessness can manifest either as persistent or scattered thoughts. It's present whenever we're caught in distraction. There may be an inability to focus— the mind rejects being directed toward one thing or jumps from one thing to the next, incapable of settling. Worry may be defined as agitated feelings of regret for what one has or hasn't done. Included in this would be imagined future problems. Being able to breathe through restlessness is a useful skill to have. Breathing consciously and paying attention to the continual rhythm of breathing in and out can calm the body and mind. With more attention given to breathing, there are fewer resources to fuel restlessness and worry.

• Doubt – Doubt is another big one that can creep into your practice. Doubt takes many forms: Doubt about the validity of the practice or, most dangerously, about oneself and one's ability to master the practice. Its simplest manifestation is a lack of clarity about the meditation instructions: *Am I doing this correctly?* Doubt can often be reasonable and convincing enough to mask its underlying causes. However, as is the case with all the other mental hindrances—sense desire, ill-will or aversion, and restlessness and worry, the antidote is the same: Return to a focus on the breath.

Let me say a little more about dullness and drowsiness, which arise from a state of tightness—a contraction of mind and body energy. So, too, does restlessness of the body or the mind. It can be very helpful, therefore, when any of these is present in your meditation practice, to find ways of opening up more space for awareness.

Tightness is usually a result of putting too much effort into focusing on the breath. Similarly, too much effort can underlie both dullness and drowsiness. Dullness is sometimes referred to as a sinking of the mind that results in a dimming of awareness. Think of it as a mental black hole, an emptiness where there's no thought, no observation of the breath, no awareness of anything. It's a gap—a formless, mental, gray area rather like dreamless sleep. A sinking mind is a void—far from the state of spaciousness that we seek in meditation.

One of the simplest ways to allow more spaciousness is to slow your breathing by taking deeper, fuller breaths, which bathes the cells in oxygen. I mention this in my first book, *Your Mitochondria—Key to Health and Longevity.* Our mitochondria require oxygen to produce ATP, the energy currency of the body. Slow, deep breathing delivers more oxygen to your cells, making you feel more energized.

For example, let's assume you've had a stressful day at the office. You've been at your desk most of the day video-conferencing and talking with associates on the phone. At the end of the day, you feel depleted but also stressed and frazzled. Most of us know that stress has a detrimental effect on our health. When you couple stress with sitting most of the day, there are negative effects on both your mental and physical health.

When we sit for long periods of time, our breathing becomes shallow. This drives hypoxia (insufficient oxygen in our cells). This lack of adequate oxygen in our cellular powerhouses releases free radicals, which cause inflammation and accelerate aging.

Coming home to your daily meditation—even when you're tired—and doing deep, slow breathing has numerous benefits. First, it helps to energize you and reduce the tightness and dullness you may be feeling. Deep breathing allows more oxygen into your cells to energize them, and it has the additional benefit of absorbing free radicals that have been created during the day as a result of stress and hypoxia.

For even greater health benefits, you may wish to add Tsa Lung meditation to your practice, which is described in Appendix 2.

Overcoming the Five Hindrances

We overcome the five hindrances through the cultivation of the five corresponding qualities of meditative stabilization: initial mental application, sustained mental application, joy, happiness, and concentration. [11]

In meditation, we're witness to our mental chatter, beliefs, and expectations. We often take pleasure and satisfaction in living in profound denial and rejection of pain and discomfort. In fact, we may hold the belief that we shouldn't suffer at all. As I indicated at the start of this chapter, living an authentic life is based on observation and acceptance of the reality of suffering. We all suffer, but suffering isn't the result of our doing something wrong for which we're being punished. Believing that suffering shouldn't happen to us is just a form of denial. Problems and difficulties are a part of life.

A natural byproduct of meditation is that we begin to see how our moment-to-moment experience is conditioned by an intricate set of causes and conditions that extend far into our past. With each inhalation and exhalation, thoughts arise. They're like clouds floating past the sun—they're that transitory and that illusory. Through the practice of meditation, we see that thoughts aren't real, they carry no inherent power, and, most importantly, they don't define who we are. Meditation allows us to see how our capacity to rest in aware presence is influenced by what we did this morning, yesterday, last week, in our relationship, in our childhood, and on and on. Again and again, we get to discover the core truth of the Buddhist teachings— that our suffering arises through our attachment to or rejection of what's happening within and around us. [12]

As we progress in our practice, we find ourselves able to observe our attachments and aversions and create space around them, so we don't hold them so tightly. These attachments and aversions are viewed as patterns in our life that are neither positive nor negative. They're simply structures that influence who we are as conditioned individuals. However, to the extent that we believe these patterns are negative and that we must alter our thinking and behavior to become our true authentic self, we can observe these patterns in terms of how they separate us from a more open, spacious, and spontaneous way of being in the world.

When we stop trying to cling to, change, or avoid thoughts, feelings, people, and situations in our life, we release the tremendous energy we expend trying to control and manipulate our experiences for more creative purposes.

As stated by Peter Fenner, "In its essential form, emptiness, spaciousness, or aware presence is the unimpeded and uncontrived expression of a content-less wisdom that instantaneously and effortlessly reveals the free and open nature of all structures of existence." [13]

References:

1. Kabat-Zinn et al.,1998; Ludwig and Kabat-Zinn, 2008; Lutz et al., 2008; Schmidt et al., 2011; Farb et al.,2012; Rosenkranz et al., 2013
2. Kaliman, P., Álvarez-López, M. J., Cosín-Tomás, M., Rosenkranz, M. A., Lutz, A., & Davidson, R. J. (2014). Rapid changes in histone deacetylases and inflammatory gene expression in expert meditators. Psychoneuroendocrinology, 40(1), 96–107.
3. Brown and Jones, 2010; Perlman et al., 2010; Grant et al., 2011; Zeidan et al., 2012; Lutz et al., 2013
4. Dusek et al., 2008; Bhasin et al., 2013), mindfulness-based stress reduction training in older adults (Creswell et al., 2012
5. Malinowski, Peter. "Neural Mechanisms of Attentional Control in Mindfulness Meditation." *Frontiers in Neuroscience* 7 (2013): 8. *PMC*. Web. 9 Feb. 2018.
6. Kaliman, P., Álvarez-López, M. J., Cosín-Tomás, M., Rosenkranz, M. A., Lutz, A., & Davidson, R. J. (2014). Rapid changes in histone deacetylases and inflammatory gene expression in expert meditators. Psychoneuroendocrinology, 40(1), 96–107.
7. Burbea, Rob. Seeing That Frees: Meditations on Emptiness and Dependent Arising (Kindle Locations 180-182). Hermes Amāra. Kindle Edition
8. Wikipedia contributors. "Pharmakon (philosophy)." Wikipedia, The Free Encyclopedia. Wikipedia, The Free Encyclopedia, 8 May. 2018. Web. 30 May. 2018.
   Heffernan, Virginia. The Muddied Meaning of 'Mindfulness'. New York Times Magazine. https://www.nytimes.com/2015/04/19/magazine/the-muddied-meaning-of-mindfulness.html
9. Burbea, Rob. Seeing That Frees: Meditations on Emptiness and Dependent Arising (Kindle Locations 1962-1966). Hermes Amāra. Kindle Edition.

10. Wallace, B. Alan. Hidden Dimensions: The Unification of Physics and Consciousness (Columbia Series in Science and Religion) (p. 65). Columbia University Press. Kindle Edition.
11. Fenner Ph.D., Peter (2007-07-01). Radiant Mind (p. 64). Sounds True. Kindle Edition.
12. Ibid., p. 175.

Chapter 8
Deepening the Experience

"You're either believing your thoughts or questioning them. There's no other choice."

-Byron Katie

As we sit in meditation, we observe the thoughts, images, beliefs, and reactions that continually emerge into consciousness. Whenever we recognize any of these patterns—which might include blaming, seeking sympathy, justifying, complaining, and explaining—this helps us minimize our identification with the problems and the associated suffering in which we habitually get caught.

I'm referring to the time and energy that we invest in trying to sort these patterns out and how that affects our lives, both internally and externally. When we stop trying to reject or avoid what we're experiencing, we release tremendous energy that can be used for creative purposes and to improve our health and extend our "healthspan"—the years of our long, healthy life.

The Power of Our Mental Constructs

Our methods for avoiding what we're experiencing are numerous and complex. We may try to deny our experience by thinking it isn't as we perceive it or that what's happening shouldn't be happening. We invest mental, emotional, and physical energy in defending or rejecting a particular interpretation of who we are and what we need. We fantasize about alternative circumstances and outcomes including strategies for self-improvement or some imagined enlightenment. We distract ourselves or numb our feelings with drugs, immersing ourselves in social media or the news, and engaging in superficial conversations. [1]

When we examine the content of our experiences, we begin to notice they're composed of images, reactions, and projections. These can be understood as mental constructs that define our view of how we, our world, and our life are. For instance, our body image represents a collection of beliefs and images that reflects how we see ourselves and how we believe others see us.

Of course, as many of us know, some of these images and beliefs are false.

Here's a vignette from my life that demonstrates how these images and beliefs play out. When I was ten or eleven years old, I was in the Boy Scouts. Every month, I received a magazine in the mail from the Boy Scouts of America organization called *Boy's Life*. In the back of the magazine was the classified section. Among the items in this section were things you could do to make money or courses you could take. One of the courses was on bodybuilding. It featured a photo of a guy looking all muscular and pumped up. I was a skinny kid, and sometimes I got picked on by older kids, so I enrolled in the course.

The important point here is that the body image I had of myself as a skinny kid with underdeveloped arms and chest is still with me today. After a shower, I sometimes look at myself in the mirror, and I hear my internal voice critiquing my arms and chest. When I go to the gym, I find myself comparing my body to that of other men.

Many of us have the belief that how we are right now isn't OK, and we look outside ourselves for a reflection of how we believe we should be. We all have areas in our lives where we do this: "I just need to tweak this part of my body a little bit," or "My hair isn't looking so good today," or whatever your usual self-criticism is. Of course, there are huge health, wellness, and beauty industries that are aware of our less-than-perfect self-images and market "fixes"—to the tune of billions of dollars a year.

As you can see from my Boy Scout vignette, to some extent, I still identify with that skinny kid, and that image defines my sense of who I am, which, in turn, creates my sense of reality. In other words, we take an image, impression, or piece of knowledge and we make it into a basic building block of our sense of self.

We might identify with a particular structure that was formed in the past and has remained in our unconscious all these years. "I'm weak," or "I'm stupid," or "I'm too emotional," or "I'm too fat," and we continue to believe throughout our life that this is true without even being conscious of it. We're living out of that identification, moment to moment, even if we're not consciously aware of it.

I'm aware of this behavior and the accompanying dialogue, but, most important, this pattern is no longer something I judge.

Observing Without Judgment

In the approach we'll be using to deepen the meditation experience, all that's required is awareness of each thought, image, or belief as it manifests in our consciousness without judgment, because judgment brings its own dark atmosphere to our mental space. It's sufficient to simply observe and acknowledge these patterns, meaning they don't require fixing. So, I don't judge myself that I still carry this belief about my body. I simple observe and accept it.

In the first section of this book, we examined beliefs that may be so ingrained in our thought process that we don't even question them anymore. They operate in the background, continuously and automatically. However, we now understand from our exploration of quantum physics and Buddhist philosophy that these patterns cause a predictable collapse of all emerging wave functions (possibilities) into the well-worn paths of a less-than-optimal life and, in the process, create suffering and stress.

Viewed essentially, images, reactions, and projections, are neither positive nor negative. These are just the building blocks we use to define ourselves as individuals within our society. However, to the extent that we believe we must alter our thinking and behavior in order to rest in our natural, spontaneous, open awareness, we can observe patterns in terms of how they disconnect us from a more spacious way of being in the world. [2]

For this discussion, I use the phrase "point of view" to collectively refer to the images, beliefs, reactions, and projections we use to define who we are. Whenever we justify a point of view or actions to others or rationalize them to ourselves, we're inadvertently expressing a limiting pattern.

Transformation Through Observation

How do we begin to discern what our patterns are? And how do we get rid of them to have a better life? First, it's vitally important to understand that there's *nothing* to get rid of and *nothing* to change. All that's required of you is a willingness to recognize these thought patterns when they arise and accept them. That sounds easy enough, right? Some patterns are obvious to us while others are subtle or deeply enmeshed and require repeated effort. And then there's the acceptance part, but we'll get to that.

Our daily meditation becomes the foundation we use to settle the mind. A settled mind allows some spaciousness into our internal chatter. From a place of spaciousness, there's more of an opportunity for observation of our thoughts and behaviors as our daily life unfolds. I want to be quick to add here that even for seasoned meditators, there are days when it's tough, if not impossible, to experience that spaciousness. But the more we practice, the easier it becomes for that spaciousness to arise.

From a place of detached observation, we begin to notice that our actions are based on our needs (our desires and attachments), and our perceptions are inherently unreliable. I know very few people who haven't experienced this in their relationships or their career. We fantasize about our happiness lying "elsewhere"—in a particular person or job or object— rather than within ourselves. Happiness is never anywhere other than where we are. [3]

For example, let's take relationships. Most of us started out believing our life would be better if only we could find a partner who was understanding enough, attractive enough, sexual enough, or _____ enough—insert whatever adjective is appropriate from a never-ending list. The assumption here is that we believe we're incomplete or unworthy, and our completeness is contingent on an external acquisition—our ideal partner.

How Suffering Works

This brings us back to the First and Second of the Four Noble Truths, which we can see aren't just archaic axioms but are playing out in our life in every moment. To restate, the first and second truths are:

The truth of suffering

The truth of the cause of suffering

We can all agree that we suffer, so there's little argument or confusion about the First Noble Truth. Some of the suffering is superficial, such as when we feel pain because we can't have the car (or house, job, relationship, gadget, etc.) that we want.

171

However, some suffering is deeply existential, such as feeling isolated or unworthy.

The Second Noble Truth tells us the cause of our suffering is our grasping or craving. Not having the amount of money we want, the relationship we think we deserve, or the happiness in our life that we believe is our birthright drives longing and a sense of deprivation. It's clear we do suffer. We feel deprived and unhappy—maybe even hopeless or resigned to our fate. If our perceived needs aren't met, we can see how the Second Noble Truth plays out—with continuous, never-satisfied grasping and craving. There's an implied demand: "It's my birthright to have a happy, fulfilled life."

Once we accept that we suffer—and this acceptance is a huge step—our journey of conscious evolution begins. We're able to cut through all pretensions and embarrassment and encounter ourselves exactly as we are—which includes, and accepts, our suffering.

The key to success in this practice is realizing that suffering isn't wrong or unfair. It's isn't something that shouldn't happen to us. We all suffer and will probably continue to do so until we die. [4] But there's much of our suffering that we can do something about—once we realize its cause and its cure.

"What's the Cause of My Suffering?"

The first step is benign acceptance—not resignation but acceptance. From this place of acceptance, we ask the next question: "What's the cause of my suffering?"

Grasping and craving (wanting what we don't have, not wanting what we do have) are clear examples. However, there are other elements that lie at the threshold of conscious and unconscious awareness, and these fundamentally shape our attachments and aversions.

172

Here's an example to make this clear. Let's say that, in our childhood, we suffered abuse. This could be physical, emotional, or sexual. This abuse may have been inflicted upon us by someone we trusted or by a stranger. Whatever the case, we carry that trauma for the rest of our life. It (the trauma) now colors our perception of reality—what we think and how we act. Often this manifests as a wariness— "I need to be vigilant and not get hurt again." In intimate relationships, there may be a concern about being too open and vulnerable, fearing we'll be betrayed or sabotaged by what we reveal to another person.

All of us long for trust, support, and nurturing. However, an early-childhood trauma of this nature can and does create a powerful conflict, wherein there's a deep craving for surrender coupled with a deep fear of what may happen if we do surrender. Often, there's no clear awareness of this fear but rather a vague feeling of vulnerability that manifests in relationships as a recurring pattern of distrust or other uncomfortable emotions but no clear sense of where this is coming from.

I use early-childhood trauma as an example because it's easy to understand how these conflicted emotions may evolve from such experiences. However, there doesn't need to be extreme, overt trauma for these fears to be established. There are many variations of how our stories, projections, and points of view form.

We have hidden (from our conscious awareness) beliefs about how life is, and these subterranean influences restrict our ability to creatively express our life. Our point of view is molded and formed by a subliminal mental process—the incessant activity of remembering, thinking, and reacting according to information and experiences from the past. In any interaction with another individual, we impose on this experience an image of who we are, who we believe they are, and a particular feeling tone on

173

our relationship with them. The result is an experience created, at least in part, by past conditioning. [5]

We're largely unaware of how our experiences interfere in our daily life because we're rarely explicitly rejecting a particular situation. What we're rejecting is the spontaneity of our behavior. We analyze and overthink everything. We hesitate, even though we may not know why. We automatically think, "No, that's not for me," and we have no idea where this aversion is coming from. This is exactly the reason for the difficulty we have in being where we are: we try to direct our experience. And, as a matter of fact, we're not just *trying* to direct our experience, we actually *do* direct it. We shape it because we're looking at it through the eyes and experiences of the past, and our life is influenced by viewing it through this filter. [6] This becomes the observational work we embark on as our meditation practice creates more openness in our life.

Cultivating Spaciousness

What's this openness I'm referring to, and how, specifically, does it help ease our suffering?

The terms "openness," "spaciousness," and "emptiness" all point to the same thing—a lessening or loosening of the mental and emotional constructs of the mind. However, the implication is that as the constructs loosen, there's a corresponding realization of the interrelatedness of all phenomena in our experience. Secondly, as the understanding of interrelatedness begins to unfold within us, the awakened mind—which is characterized by qualities like wisdom, compassion, clarity, and courage—begins to emerge. But I want to be perfectly clear: The awakened mind has always been present; it's just been drowned out by all our internal chatter, patterns, and beliefs.

Peter Fenner points to this clarity in his book, *Radiant Mind*: "The experience of unconditioned awareness also heals by percolating through the layers of our habitual conditioning and changing its structure, dissolving fixations and attachments, and possibly even producing a radical reorientation of our experience of reality. We become clearer, more open, and less reactive and defensive — and hence better able to release our fears and insecurities." [7]

So, we have a working definition of openness or spaciousness, which leaves us with the second half of the question: "How does this spaciousness help ease our suffering?"

Suffering can be viewed as a symptom, a message emerging from our authentic self, which is our truest guide. Our suffering beckons us to explore and challenge our deeply held beliefs and projections about who we are, which is the path to finding our way to peace. Through examining and questioning our suffering, we come into greater contact with our authentic, caring, creative, strong, loving self, which is inextricably connected with all humanity, all life.

The Two Causes of Suffering

There are two broad categories of suffering. The first category contains everything outside of our control that causes us suffering. Take the hurricanes that happened in 2017, in Houston and Puerto Rico, which caused much suffering for so many people. This category of suffering also includes the passing of loved ones, either naturally or unexpectedly, or being diagnosed with an illness. Additionally, we'll include in this category the countless people who are suffering on our planet because of famine or displacement as the result of wars or ethnic cleansing. We live our life from the viewpoint that we're the captain of our ship, and then something catastrophic happens to us that profoundly takes us out of that illusion and causes deep suffering. (Please see the appendix on Hell Realms).

The Reality We Create

The second category of suffering—which causes the majority of the discomfort we experience in our life—is suffering we create for ourselves. This is specifically the area this book deals with—recognizing how we create our own suffering and—by developing insight and acceptance of our suffering—how we can free ourselves from it.

I want to be as clear as possible here. I'm not talking about another get-well project. Nothing is wrong with you that needs to be corrected. Don't take the statement, "recognizing how we create our own suffering," to mean there's something wrong with you that needs to be fixed. Take a deep breath and understand that this approach is based on understanding and acceptance.

Let's discuss some of the ways we create suffering for ourselves. Possibly some of these are familiar companions in your life.

1. Beliefs and judgments – Our beliefs and judgments are numerous and treacherous. They cause much suffering for us because they're seamlessly integrated into our life. We assume many of these beliefs to be absolute truths and, when we're challenged or questioned about them, we may notice a strong emotional response arising. The strong emotional response is a giveaway that we're stuck in a limiting belief or judgment.

2. Blaming – Probably one of our favorite allies is blaming ourselves or others for situations that don't turn out the way we want. Underneath the blaming is a demand— "I want it to be different!" Our ways of blaming ourselves and others come in many forms: "I never have any good luck," or "She could have avoided this by listening to me more carefully," or "This clearly means I'm an inadequate person," or "It's her fault. She always acts this way."

3. Stories – We all have a story we can drop into at a moment's notice. Significantly, we can often see how our story (and

thus also ourselves, who are necessarily central to the story) imprisons and disempowers us. For instance, we see our story casts us as a victim in some way. For many people, seeing themselves as the victim feels authentic and justified, but it's a perception that blinds us to our true power. If we're locked into our story and believe the fantasy of our self-identity that it creates is true, this leaves no freedom to create a different story of ourselves and our life. We're unable to have experiences of letting go of our way of looking and seeing through other lenses—and this creates ongoing suffering.

4. Sexuality – Most of us have deeply held beliefs about intimacy and sexuality, some of which were formed by our past experiences and some that were imposed by society. Sexuality, by its nature, involves surrender and intimate contact with "the other." Many of us associate loss of control and vulnerability with weakness or as emotionally risky. Past experiences may set the stage for fantasies that always result in disappointment, a sense of alienation, or even sadomasochist behaviors, which may be coupled with deep shame. It's these feelings of shame, weakness, and a desire to be cruel that restrict our creative sexual energies.

5. Health – The belief that we're contained within our body, bounded by our body, or identified as our body is a major source of suffering. This attachment to the body brings up ongoing worry about our health and wellbeing—another source of suffering. Our attachment to our body—and our concerns about its wellbeing—is simply an expression of fear about our mortality. We can't do anything about our mortality, but we can improve the quality and length of our life, which includes learning how to reduce our suffering.

6. Feeling inadequate because we can't achieve what we think we want – Maybe you grew up in a family where there was pressure to achieve, and that carries over as a sense of unworthiness or presumed failure in your day-to-day

activities. You find it difficult to relax, let go, and stop striving. You may not even take the time to assess whether what you think you want is, in fact, what you really want. This inner voice to do and be a particular thing is what drives you. Added to that are bombardments from society and the media to aspire to a particular lifestyle with the promise that having certain material things will make you feel like you've "made it" and take away your suffering.

7. Lack of awareness of how our actions affect those around us – This comes up most clearly in relationships and at work. When your significant other tells you that you've hurt them, pay attention to the place that wants to defend yourself or a sudden hardening of your heart that says, "I don't care."

8. Past trauma in your life – We've already discussed how past trauma can affect our everyday life in overt or subtle ways. You may have had therapy to address this experience, but the real issue is: Is the trauma still being played out in your life, influencing your decisions, and creating ongoing suffering?

9. Money – This one is also a dear friend to many of us, because we've grown up in a culture that ties our sense of self-worth to how much money we have. Regardless of what you acquire or achieve, if you operate from an impoverished perspective ("I'm not rich enough") you'll always perceive yourself as poverty-stricken. This doesn't just relate to actual cash in the bank. You might be seeking the value of your father's approval or that of a lover, or the value associated with success in your work, or even "enlightenment." All of these are forms of acquisition and gaining perceived value, so, in that sense, it's the same as with money. In all seeking, and in the activity inherent in seeking, there's an assumption that you're deficient. [8]

10. Spirituality – This is another area that may start with a belief that we're deficient and causes us to pursue a path of

continually trying to reach closer communion with God or a more enlightened place. This can be further compounded if our upbringing was heavily influenced by a religion that made us believe we were unworthy or even sinful if we didn't believe in God.

An Exercise in Getting to Know Your Authentic Self

Over the next week, take some time each day and complete one or more of the following statements:

- My body is. . .
- When I think about my health, I . . .
- I notice I feel like blaming (myself or someone else) when...
- I feel inadequate about . . .
- When I think about money I feel. . .
- I feel vulnerable when I remember certain events in the past, such as. . .
- At work I feel overwhelmed when/by . . .
- I notice that when one of my beliefs is questioned I feel . . .

In this exercise, you're acknowledging your future suffering—not as something that must happen but as something that will, in all likelihood, continue to occur until you begin to understand what causes you to suffer and how to short-circuit that process.

In our practice, we must be willing to examine things within ourselves and our lives that are problematic, selfish, and reactive. We can't try to deny them or distract ourselves from them. Instead, we need to acknowledge and confront difficulties and delusions and learn to deal with them. We need to learn to recognize all that's beautiful within us as well as our fears, vulnerabilities, and inadequacies. That's how we discover our authentic self. [9]

Our Hidden Inner World

The first thing you realize when you begin to meditate is, "Wow, I have a lot of thoughts and images going on." Along with this observation is the realization that you're having internal conversations with yourself and others. Now, of course, you've always been having conversations with yourself. Everyone does, but often this is only brought "out in the open," as it were, during the process of meditation. By out in the open, I mean observed.

Peter Fenner nicely elucidates this: "I use the term 'conversation' to refer to both the audible interactions we have with other people and the silent conversations we have with ourselves. In this sense, we're nearly always in conversation. In silent conversations, we're both the speaker and the listener as we listen to the stream of what our own thoughts are speaking. We're in silent conversations with ourselves about what is happening, what has happened, what we could do, should do." [10]

Within our inner conversations, we can further identify exchanges we have with ourselves and with others. Conversations with others occur when we're trying to work through an interaction, either past or future. Maybe you have an upcoming meeting with your boss, and you're trying out different scenarios of what to say, how to respond. Other times, the conversation may be reassessing a difficult interaction you had with someone and rescripting the incident using directives such as, "If I'd only said this," or "If only I hadn't gotten angry." In these inner dialogues, we speculate about or anticipate how another might respond to what we say or do.

Often these imagined dialogues appear as movies in our mind—a fully scripted piece in which we're directing as well as playing the lead role. Just like in a good movie, we hope to evoke a powerful emotional response or otherwise exert our influence—which means we're in control of the scene. The point is that imagery causes specific feelings to arise and, when we meditate, this imagery can hijack our attention, especially if the imagery is about something heavy like sexuality. Such thoughts condition the space around the imagery, especially if there's been trauma, frightening events, or a repressive household environment in childhood.

We must remind ourselves, again and again, that our purpose in meditation is to observe and accept all that arises—whether the thoughts and images are sublime or vile. This is what's sometimes referred to as training the mind—we're training ourselves to recognize that thoughts are just thoughts. They may seem more compelling than anything in our lives at times, but they're transitory. What we have a strong feeling about today may not even cause a blip on our emotional scale a week from now.

How to Work with Unpleasant or Alarming Thoughts, Memories, and Images

It's shocking when unpleasant images appear in our mind, and our initial response is to stop thinking about them coupled with a quick inner admonition that we should feel disgust and concern (for ourselves) that such a thought inhabits our psyche. No matter the nature of the thought, however seemingly debased, we don't judge it as being virtuous or nonvirtuous. [11]

Let's expand this discussion so we can have a better understanding of how to deal with upsetting material when it arises. Initially in our meditative practice, the focus is on our breathing. At that level, when dialogue or images—including disturbing images—arise, we immediately return to our breathing, so we don't go down the rabbit hole of engaging with that dialogue or image. The practice is one of observation without engagement coupled with focusing on the breath. Of course, there will be times when we slip and find ourselves lost in a narrative provoked by an image. When we realize this has happened, we simply return to watching our breathing.

To be clear, all of us, at times, have unkind thoughts about ourselves and others or thoughts that may objectify and categorize someone. When this happens, we don't spend our time and energy defending or chastising ourselves, engaging in lectures about how we're never going to get enlightened if we keep having uncharitable thoughts. When we notice those thoughts, images, and stories, we simply drop them. This process of "just drop it" will, like magic, retrain our mind to not follow our thoughts and stories.

Most of the images that arise during meditation are founded in our own life experience, but some may not have anything to do with us. In the chapters on quantum physics and Buddhist philosophy, we discussed the concept of emptiness and how that brings us into a fundamental understanding of the interrelatedness of all phenomena. Nothing arises in isolation. Further, we discussed that our individual knowledge has emerged from a consciousness that connects and pervades everything. This is in direct contradiction to what science purports—that consciousness is a property of our individual brains.

From this understanding, we can address the sources of images that may arise during meditation. Throughout history, there has been extreme barbarism and cruelty, which continues to this day in the form of torture, murder, slavery, kidnapping, starvation, and genocide. This imagery persists through time as part of the collective human consciousness. It doesn't help that we're bombarded by the media with images of these activities.

When this material arises—whether it's your stuff or the world's stuff—you're invited to deconstruct it, a process that we'll discuss in the next chapter. Because we're all part of the world, all stuff is ultimately our stuff, which brings us full circle to the interrelatedness of all phenomena and why it only makes sense that we cultivate compassion and empathy for every suffering being in our world.

Identification Versus the Authentic Self

Each of us hold views of ourselves that we take to be our authentic self. In doing this observation work, we begin to understand that these views are self-constructed and only exist as imaginary projections in the mind. By being aware of these projections, a significant measure of liberation and ease are made available to us.

Most of our self-views are constructed from what we identify with. We could be identifying with a view or projection we have about how we should emotionally respond in a given situation or how we should behave in a relationship or at work or with our parents or children. Depending on the circumstances, we find ourselves identifying with many different ideas of what we should think or how we should behave.

Equating these identifications—which are characteristics of the body and mind—with our essential self is a false belief. Beliefs and projections are artifacts of our mind, not who we truly are, and cause us to live a narrow, confined life as a result.

What we seek, then, are both the means of recognizing the inherent emptiness of our petrified beliefs and assumptions and the ability to move out of the narrative mode so that more truthful insights can arise. Part of this process is understanding how a particular self-view has been constructed, which allows us to see through it.

We tend to identify most strongly with our body—in particular, our physical appearance. We believe we're too short, too tall, too fat or skinny, our tummy's too big, our hair's too curly or straight or insufficient, we're starting to get wrinkles around our eyes, our skin is sagging—on and on. This deep identification with our appearance is powerfully influenced by society and marketing, and it's very seductive. It's no wonder we so easily adopt this particular identification.

Other strong sources of identification are our job, our gender, our nationality, our race, or how smart we think we are. Some people identify with being an abused child, and that becomes their primary identity throughout life. Fundamentally, whatever is truly real isn't created or sustained by our identification with it. [13]

As I mentioned, in the next chapter, we'll explore methods to dismantle these identifications and projections. The underlying imperative in this exploration is, "Question everything." Consider this, for example: When we hear from our doctor that we have a serious illness or require surgery of some kind, it isn't uncommon to seek another opinion. It's always a good idea when it comes to our health to find out what another professional has to say about our situation. It should be the same with what we identify with. If you become aware of an identification, notice how you feel when you recognize it. Do you judge it, reject it, feel relieved, become curious? Once you begin exploring it, notice if your sense of identification shifts, dissolves, or transforms over time.

Let's review, then, how we move toward a deeper understanding of our day-to-day experience and become more authentic and expressive of who we really are. We see that when we examine the mental content of our experience, we notice it's composed of images, reactions, and projections created in our mind. For instance, the body image that we rely on to experience ourselves is manufactured solely within our own mind. We may think what we see in the mirror is that image, and that it's independent of our perception of it, but that's untrue. We see ourselves differently than other people see us, and, if we pay attention, we're aware that our perception of our body changes all the time. Today we think we look OK and tomorrow we're full of criticism.

Generally speaking, we cling to various permutations of self-conception–either explicitly or intuitively—through our normal ways of looking. Sometimes we may conceive of ourselves as one or more of what Buddhism refers to as the five aggregates: form, sensations, perceptions, mental activity or formations (thoughts), and consciousness. At times, we may identify with the body as ourselves, or the mind, or one aspect of the mind such as emotion or intelligence: "I'm an angry/sad/fearful person" or "I'm a smart person." Another kind of identification is perceiving the self as somehow other than the aggregates but possessing them–owning the body, the mind, the emotions, perceptions, or other mental factors. [14]

As greater clarity, greater understanding, and greater awareness of presence and spaciousness arise, we begin to more actively question what's going on in our mind when we think we're being ourselves. We begin to discern that what we're engaged in is a reaction or projection of our mind onto the moment. More specifically, we begin to see the inner activity of projections, stories, beliefs, and judgments—which we'd been accustomed to believing were reality.

As we investigate more deeply, we recognize that our inner landscape, our "world," is essentially the same wherever we are—at home, at work, on vacation. It's the same ol' familiar projections, stories, and beliefs. As the saying goes, "Wherever you go, there you are," because "you" (your mind) is always with you. Each of us lives in a world of conditioned inner and outer experiences—that is to say, appearances–sights, sounds, smells, tastes, bodily sensations, emotions, thoughts, memories, dreams, and intentions. We begin to understand that the space we live and move in is heavily conditioned to create a predictable collapse of the wave function—i.e., habitual thoughts and behaviors. Having a life of greater freedom, more spontaneity, creativity, openness, caring, and authenticity can only occur when there's an ongoing questioning of what we believe to be real. Viewing ourselves through a lens of deconstruction frees up our perceptions—it cleanses the lens. We see that nothing in the world is as solid and unchanging as we may have assumed it to be.

A Path of No Hope

This may have been a difficult chapter for some readers. Aspects of our inner landscape may cause us shame, and we may do anything to keep those secrets, even from ourselves, by repressing them when they arise into our awareness. In the approach of meditation we've been discussing—that of observation and awareness—nothing is judged as sacred or profane. Everything is welcomed into awareness, because this is the only way we can deal with and release thoughts and feelings that cause us suffering. This doesn't mean we dwell on these thoughts or images. Our goal is to observe them like we observe a cloud passing in front of the sun. We watch but don't grasp, react, or resist. We gently observe each thought and image as it passes and then vanishes out of our awareness.

I hear you saying, "Well, that sounds lovely, but how does one just passively relive the images of being physically abused or constantly belittled? Nobody who's suffered that kind of trauma is ever going to be able to replay those images and not have a strong reaction." Actually, it is possible. I know this because many people have done it. Our shames, our regrets, our guilt aren't unique to us. These feelings are part of the human condition. But there are tools and practices to free ourselves of these torments, and I've included two of them, Tsa Lung meditation (Appendix 2) and Brainspotting (Appendix 3).

As mentioned, the approach we use is first settling the mind. In this state, spaciousness arises in our consciousness and, in this spacious place, we allow all thoughts, images, and feelings to come into our minds. With a willingness to accept whatever arises—including the part of you that wants to deny it—the emotional hold these thoughts and memories have begins to dissipate. By dissipate, I don't mean the thoughts and images disappear but rather the emotional charge around them lessens. You begin to understand that just because a difficult thought or image arises, this says nothing about who you really are.

Our path on this meditative journey is ultimately a path of no hope. When I tell people this, they look at me with alarm. But if you consider what I'm saying, I think you'll understand the true meaning. When our life isn't so preoccupied with how our past, our beliefs, and our projections are affecting our current life—and, as a consequence, with hoping and wishing the future will be different—we're more present in our life. Without these hopes, we find ourselves seated in the present moment and living our life in the NOW.

In reality, you've always lived your life in the Now, because it couldn't be otherwise. But that Now may have been clouded by your fears, regrets, self-judging, and all these other mental projections that prevented you from seeing what's right in front of you—and what's right in front of you is never the past or the future. Being present is an eyes-open meditation, which we'll discuss in the next chapter.

As you become more present in your life, a radical change occurs. Your continuous wishing and hoping for your life to be different lessens. Take a moment and reflect on this statement: "As you are right now is enough." Right now, you're reading this book. Probably your mind chatter is fairly quiet. Take a breath and ask yourself this question: "Right now, in this moment, am I OK?" It may surprise you to find out the answer. Wherever you are and whoever you're with and whatever you're doing—even if you've held the belief that your life is a mess—in this one, single moment, you're OK. That may change in the next second, but in this moment, you feel complete.

Resting in the moment, just being present fully in your life, radically reduces hoping. This hope may not be in the form of an overt statement such as "I hope I get a better job," or "I hope my partner starts loving me again," or "I hope I win the lottery." This hope may be a vague longing for more meaning. But that's a good thing. Realizing you want more meaning in your life isn't the same as hope, which implies you have little agency over what happens to you. You can find more meaning, and it requires only a willingness to cultivate a spacious mind. This light of awareness brings us into the reality of the moment. At the same time, it illuminates who we really are, not what we believe ourselves to be. [15]

Over the long term, repeated and regular immersion in presence and spaciousness supports the emergence of a steadiness of genuine confidence. We come to know, beyond doubt, that happiness is possible for us in this life. And because this deep happiness we experience is originating within us, we begin to feel less vulnerable to and dependent on the uncertainties of changing external conditions. We let go of expecting and hoping that our suffering will be relieved by others, or the acquisition of material things, or a run of good luck, and we walk a path of no hope.

References:

1. Fenner, Peter. Radiant Mind (p. 163). Sounds True. Kindle Edition.
2. Fenner, Peter. (n.d.). Dismantling fixations. Retrieved from http://www.radiantmind.net/dismantling-fixations/
3. Fenner, Peter. Radiant Mind (p. 137). Sounds True. Kindle Edition.
4. Fenner, Peter. Radiant Mind (p. 162). Sounds True. Kindle Edition.
5. Almaas, A. H. The Unfolding Now: Realizing Your True Nature through the Practice of Presence (Kindle Locations 2186-2199). Shambhala Publications. Kindle Edition.
6. Ibid, (Kindle Locations 2186-2199).
7. Fenner Ph.D., Peter. Radiant Mind (p. 18). Sounds True. Kindle Edition.
8. Almaas, A. H. Diamond Heart: Book Four: Indestructible Innocence, (pg. 23), Shambhala Publications, Kindle Edition
9. Almaas, A. H. (2011-07-12). Diamond Heart: Book Five: Inexhaustible Mystery (Locations 3112-3115). Shambhala Publications. Kindle Edition.
10. Fenner Ph.D., Peter. Radiant Mind (p. 149). Sounds True. Kindle Edition.
11. Brown Ph.D., Daniel; Robert Thurman (2006-10-10). Pointing Out the Great Way: The Stages of Meditation in the Mahamudra Tradition (p. 410). Wisdom Publications. Kindle Edition.
12. Burbea, Rob. Seeing That Frees: Meditations on Emptiness and Dependent Arising (Kindle Locations 2231-2237). Hermes Amāra. Kindle Edition
13. Almaas, A. H. The Unfolding Now: Realizing Your True Nature through the Practice of Presence (Kindle Locations 2491-2493). Shambhala Publications. Kindle Edition.

14. Burbea, Rob. Seeing That Frees: Meditations on Emptiness and Dependent Arising (Kindle Locations 2847-2852). Hermes Amāra. Kindle Edition.
15. Almaas, A. H. The Unfolding Now: Realizing Your True Nature through the Practice of Presence (Kindle Locations 2218-2235). Shambhala Publications. Kindle Edition.

Chapter 9
Deconstructing Our Conditioned Views

"To realize your true nature, you must wait for the right moment and the right conditions."

Chinese Zen master Pai-Chang (720 – 814)

We've come a long way in explaining how our thoughts define us and, over time, can become habituated and restrict our life and health. In this chapter, we present an approach infused with the rich legacy of Buddhist meditation practices that will help to dismantle some of the thick overlay of mental structures that prevent us from moving into greater openness—bringing us to a life in which our experience is more free of feelings, thoughts, perceptions, and interpretations that limit us and cause us a good deal of suffering.

These structures and interpretations obscure the clear, direct experience of what's occurring in our life moment to moment. As I suggested in Part One, this greater openness or spaciousness is permeated with consciousness which is always present, whether we're aware of it or not. With greater spaciousness, we find ourselves resting in a vast awareness that's infinitely larger than the space of our own psyche. It's this vastness we call consciousness that nourishes our body and mind, allows our creativity to emerge, and fills us with love and compassion. We closely observe whatever arises within this space with discerning intelligence but without modifying, censoring, or editing in any way.

Thoughts are always spontaneously arising in our mind. Most of the time, thoughts arise as responses from the past, as we've discussed. However, there are also spontaneous, original thoughts that can and do arise in the present moment. This could be an insight, a creative inspiration, or an intuitive feeling to reach out to someone. It's our rigid structures and beliefs that prevent us from experiencing the fresh and open mind in which these creative thoughts can arise and be recognized.

A Practice to Deconstruct Our Views

Views are perspectives and attitudes to which we become attached. They give rise to confusion and inhibit our ability to be mentally calm and still. Because of the depth and force of our views, it's normal for us, without practice, to remain trapped in views of ourselves—locked into our identities—at least at some level. For complex reasons, a great deal of the pain that people experience in our modern culture occurs at what might be called the personality and relational level of the self–how we think about, feel, and see ourselves as we interact with others. [1]

Each of us has and believes in ideas about how things should be—for instance, what constitutes happiness and success. We're always trying to live our life according to these ideas. But these beliefs close us off from the openness that will reveal what's actually possible.

First, we need to come to the place where we realize that behind every experience of suffering lies resistance. We're either resisting what we have in our life or resisting losing it. When we identify what we're resisting and let go, we're on the way to becoming free and complete.

From a view of nonresistance, we naturally question ourselves and our life. This may be one reason you're reading this book. But what's your motivation? Isn't your motivation that there's something you want and you're trying to find out how to go about getting it?

Wanting something is fine and represents a creative expression of ourselves. However, it's from the thick overlay of our beliefs and conditioned ideas that this creative expression emerges. Every day, you operate under the same habits, ideas, and hopes. Essentially, we carry our past with us, and this past, coupled with our beliefs and projections, profoundly influences our future. And, truthfully, there's a place in us that wants things to continue as they have been. Most of us like at least a certain amount of routine. We don't like change and uncertainty. And this is exactly why transformation eludes us.

I think Bert, of Bert and Ernie from Sesame Street, said it best: "Ernie, you got to put down the ducky if you want to play the saxophone."

(https://www.youtube.com/watch?v=acBixR_JRuM

Courtesy: http://www.sesamestreet.org)

Examining our views allows us to accept our suffering. As this acceptance emerges in our practice, we cut through the illusion that suffering means something is wrong with us.

Begin with Meditation

The initial approach to begin to identify and deconstruct our views is silent meditation, which allows more spaciousness into our consciousness by settling or quieting our mind. I'm going to introduce you to a range of inquiry techniques drawn from the 2500-year lineage of Buddhist meditation traditions. These different deconstructive conversations can merge and blend into each other. Sometimes one inquiry doesn't work, or you're doing one inquiry and it blends into another. Don't worry. However, I said you'd only need to devote 20 minutes a day to meditation, and it would improve both your health and your creativity. So how can I add another dimension to that without adding more time?

The Reality We Create

As you know, we spend a good deal of our mental time questioning, comparing, complaining, wishing, and evaluating everything going on outside and inside of us. In this approach, we're going to take a little of that mental time and use it to engage in a more focused, introspective observation and conversation. We'll couple this with our settled mind, positive will, and compassion toward ourselves to gain insight and awareness concerning our true identity—that which isn't defined by our past or societal views and projections. It's critical to remember that no matter how completely our self-image has become an ingrained aspect of our sense of self, it's nevertheless a construct of the mind.

The techniques we'll be introducing are:

• The Essential Question

• Inquiry

• Choosing a Simpler Object of Attention

• Points of View and Positions

• How Things Are

• Presence

• Walking Meditation

All of these lead us to a wonderful destination—our authentic self.

The Essential Question

The essential question is always, "Am I suffering right now, in this moment?" Suffering, as we've defined it in this book, could be stress, anger, depression, pain (either physical or emotional), tightness (of body or mind), or melancholy. Mindful observation reveals that any craving or clinging is always accompanied by, and reflected in, blocks and knots in the physical body.

194

For the essential question, if "suffering" seems too general of a term, substitute another word that's more specific: "Am I sad/stressed/anxious in this moment?" Make the question real for you.

In our Western society, suffering isn't viewed favorably, and rarely is it shown to be not only a natural part of life but a step along the path toward awareness. Considerable effort is made by the culture to promote a lifestyle of consumption—but, as most of us eventually realize, consumption has nothing to do with achieving genuine happiness. The belief that we need "more" creates deep, unresolved yearnings and, in our society, we keep on striving and consuming even as we recognize we're no happier. The message we receive goes something like this: "Just keep focused on the goal (a better job, better relationship, more money, etc.) and ignore or tolerate the suffering. Eventually (someday in the future) you'll get what you want if you just keep at it." Does this reasoning sound familiar?

One of the big steps on this journey is to accept that we do suffer, and it doesn't mean anything is wrong because we suffer. The practice of deconstruction helps diminish our suffering by expanding our awareness. As you gain awareness about the nature of your suffering, there's a corresponding realization that begins to permeate your consciousness: suffering is a profound teacher.

The essential question brings us to embrace our suffering in the Now. This question of facing one's suffering is of immense importance. Why? Because those areas of suffering we're closed off from or ignore drive the disease process.

We ask the essential question any time we notice any of the types of suffering mentioned above—stress, anger, depression, pain, etc. Here's the tricky part. As I said, we've become really good at enduring or ignoring our suffering. For example, our relationship may feel hopeless: "This is not the person I want to be with." Yet, we endure it, hoping something will change and, in the interim, we create a story to explain why we stay. We may suffer in our job. Every day, we go to work, feel stressed, and tell ourselves that's just part of the job and if we want to reach our goal of more money or self-esteem, we have to endure it.

How does asking the essential question free us from suffering? From the examples I just gave, you may notice a part of you that says. "Geez, I don't want to feel that—it's too painful," or "I'm just doing what it takes to get what I want." What's implied in the question is courage, strength, and compassion for one's self. This means we have the courage to examine ourselves; we have compassion, so we don't judge ourselves when we recognize a place of suffering; and we have the strength to immediately not retreat into the story about why we're suffering. Really, what's involved in asking the essential question is simply recognizing that presence includes being aware of the thoughts, feelings, and memories we'd prefer not to acknowledge.

Again, this exercise in deconstructing your views is about observation and awareness. You aren't being asked to change. Just bring awareness into those areas that have become habituated or deadened to your suffering. When our conditioned way of being—our beliefs, values, and preferences, and their related stories—is the basis for our identity, the initial step of bringing awareness into these areas is powerful, and the essential question does that.

Often, when I'm doing this exercise with people, they take time to consider the question. Then, at some point, they inhale and exhale deeply, with a corresponding relaxation of the body. This represents a simple acknowledgment being made internally: "Oh, this is where I'm suffering," and nothing else needs to be done.

It's important to notice if you immediately overlay the exposed suffering with a story. It's OK if this happens—as long as you notice it. You need do nothing except observe it. These observations provide us with insight into where we may have an attachment to suffering or a habitual need to create a reason why we're suffering or distract ourselves from it. Creating a reason for our suffering generally involves blaming others or attributing our suffering to some outside circumstance.

It's difficult to rest in a place of suffering, so our instinct is to find something to occupy or distract us, so we don't feel the pain. Always escaping into "doing" rather than "being" (with the suffering) can become habituated. In fact, it's almost a cultural requirement in this country to keep ourselves busy and distracted.

Finally, I want to point out that when you ask yourself the essential question, you may find you have no suffering in that moment. Even though you were suffering five minutes ago, and you may even believe you're suffering now, it could happen that, in the moment you ask the question, the suffering disappears.

Inquiry

Inquiry is another method we can use when we notice a judgment come up or an emotional response emerge, and we're curious about it. Inquiry doesn't necessarily mean we're always in deep contemplation about our lives or coming up with more and more questions. Maybe we notice we weren't very open in an interaction we had with someone. We don't understand our response, and we want to investigate it. The ongoing practice becomes a time for developing more awareness of our experience and recognizing when we're transparent and when we're opaque. Our goal is to inquire from a place of curiosity and compassion toward ourselves. [2]

What's the process by which inquiry occurs? Any time we feel upset or bothered by an interaction is a good opportunity to do an inquiry. We begin by asking ourselves what's true in the experience. For example, I may acknowledge that what's true is I don't like the way a friend is ignoring me. It's not unusual for stuff from our childhood to creep into our relationships with others, and the inquiry process includes questioning if the situation reflects a familiar element from our past.

As I've indicated, this familiarity causes the same, predictable collapse of the wave function into an all-too-familiar pattern. How we felt as a child doesn't need to dictate how we respond today. Through inquiry, we see that what we take as the truth may, in fact, be a projection and false. With this understanding, we become present in the moment and aren't living in the past. This cultivation of presence resets the wave function. Sometimes, this is an immediate reset and we never go down that old familiar path again. Other times, it can take a while. There's a delayed response and we just keep reminding ourselves, "Oops, here I am again in this familiar pattern." We experience this awareness with compassion toward ourselves and without judgment.

Here's a sample situation:

You notice you're feeling _____ (insert an emotion: hurt, angry, depressed, sad, lonely, indignant). You bring yourself into alignment with the feeling you're having in the moment. Alignment means you're clearly acknowledging the feeling that's being evoked. Specifically, within the myriad thoughts and stories around the incident, you're narrowing the focus to your truth.

You then take a couple of slow, deep breaths and say to yourself, "I'm feeling (insert the feeling). There's nothing wrong with this feeling, nor is this feeling a reflection of anything wrong with me." With just these two steps, you've brought yourself into the present and, in many cases, that's enough. The story dissolves.

Consider this – Many times, our internal chatter is tightly woven and repetitive. Think of the times something has gotten you upset and your sleep gets disrupted as you go over and over the incident in your mind. Your feelings remain in the background and the repetitive story takes the forefront. Sometimes, getting in touch with the feeling isn't sufficient to dissolve the story, and an additional step is needed. All feelings have a thought attached to them. A thought could be a statement of belief that your suffering will continue into the future. For example, if you're feeling depressed, you believe that depression will continue indefinitely into the future, or, if you're lonely, you'll never find someone.

Ask yourself this question – What thought is evoking this feeling? This is another essential question. We need to be careful here, as it's easy to drop quickly back into the story. The story is what "the other" said or did to you. From this place of inquiry—which brings awareness into these areas that have become petrified—we don't take what's being described as true. What seems to be happening may actually not be happening. Meaning, when the thought coupled to the feeling is examined, we may find it isn't true and, in the moment, there's no suffering, just the petrified view that we've repeated over and over.

The process of inquiry permeates our entire consciousness, not just the specific area we're inquiring into. It develops a global awareness of our thoughts and actions—in other words, mindfulness. As we inquire into different areas of our life, we start recognizing patterns. As we see the patterns, they become objects of inquiry.

The practice of inquiry has no goals. We inquire without judgment and with no intention to "get rid of" or diminish the pain or suffering we may be experiencing. Sitting in the truth of the moment as it unfolds allows us to become aware of our desires and beliefs. This ability to inquire without the expectation of going anywhere or fixing anything allows insight to spontaneously emerge. Insight, as used here, means that understanding arises. For example, when I felt ignored by my friend, the insight may have been that I want to be seen and that this isn't a gentle statement but a strong demand.

An insight of this nature has the ability to clear psychonoetic thought forms, which are clusters of thought forms nested together within a central belief at the quantum level, and result in resetting the collapse of the probability wave. Insight into a strong demand to be seen releases awareness throughout our mind, which allows for compassion toward oneself to arise. In addition, understanding of and compassion for our friend also emerges. She may, in fact, have been preoccupied with her own internal struggles, and, as the saying goes, her behavior had nothing to do with me. Realizing this allows compassion and acceptance to permeate our consciousness—both toward our self and others.

We don't inquire or do practice to change. That's not the point. When we recognize that we're disturbed or upset, we see we've been offered a gift rather than a burden. Through inquiry, we have the opportunity to become more fully present in our life rather than living under the weight of fixed beliefs and conditioning from our past.

I suggest a more structured approach to your inquiry because, in reality, we already have an internal, ongoing inquiry taking place. As we've discussed, we all have ongoing internal conversations with ourselves, some of them quite lively! One kind of internal conversation—using the example of the friend who ignored me—could involve a discussion I might have with her about feeling ignored. Typically, these "discussions" involve us venting and blaming the other person. A variation of this conversation would be questioning myself about why I tolerated that behavior in my friend. Both of these conversations are unkind toward myself (because I may lose my friend by blaming). However, using inquiry, we can deconstruct our beliefs in these imaginary conversations. These conversations can be used to dismantle our conditioning and entrenched positions to further explore the seeming reality of our own reactive feelings and emotions. In the case of what I perceived as the insensitivity of my friend, I could inquire what her behavior triggered in me and where that response came from.

Inquiry into ourselves is approached in an open-hearted way. In other words, we don't do this to designate blame or continue "the story." Byron Katie, in her book, *Loving What Is: Four Questions That Can Change Your Life*, has a nice way of beginning the inquiry: "I can find only three kinds of business in the universe: mine, yours, and God's. (For me, the word God means 'reality.' Reality is God, because it rules. Anything that's out of my control, your control, and everyone else's control—I call that God's business.) To think that I know what's best for anyone else is to be out of my business. Even in the name of love, it is pure arrogance, and the result is tension, anxiety, and fear. Do I know what's right for me? That is my only business. Let me work with that before I try to solve your problems for you." [3]

Inquiry can lead to dismantling our conditioned structures and bring us into open awareness without judgements or beliefs. Let's say you're feeling troubled and you start questioning (inquiry). Maybe you start with Byron Katie's approach to sort out whose business this is. In doing inquiry, you sometimes find you're definitely in someone else's business. There's nothing wrong with this, but it's an important observation to have.

For example, if you're a parent, you could be concerned with your child's course of action and you have opinions about how he should be doing things. Clearly, you're in someone else's business, and I'm sure your kid will make you aware of that. However, as you begin to explore and get beneath the structured overlay of "shoulds," you become aware of a deeper level of love, concern, and fear—the deep love a parent has for a child and the concern and fear that something could happen and that you have limited control in your child's life. To the degree that we can sit with these feelings and tolerate the helplessness of looking into the void and accepting our lack of control, a deeper foundation of support is found. It's a foundation that's always existed in you, but it's been obscured by a thick overlay of conditioned responses and beliefs.

This foundation is comprised of open awareness (without judgements, beliefs, or "shoulds"), compassion, strength, love, and trust. It contains an understanding of your interrelatedness and interdependence with all life. With this understanding, you realize it's OK to be concerned about your child. However, what's missing is the hard demand that you figure it out. Understand that what I'm doing here is considered a pointing exercise. What I'm pointing to—this foundation—fundamentally can't be described, so it's difficult to talk about it. It's not someplace to get to because it isn't separate from you.

Any experience of presence can change your perspective and your view of reality. For example, think about a time when you were overwhelmed by compassion. Not only did it affect your experience of yourself but also how you perceived everything else. That feeling of compassion can change your attitude, your priorities, and your goals. You probably felt kindness toward your own experience and felt more sensitive to the struggles in others' lives. [4]

The intent of inquiry isn't to do something about it (the experience) but only to observe it. The implication is it's like a seed thought dropped into consciousness to grow and proliferate. It's well known in Buddhist philosophy that these experiences of spaciousness and insight do arise, and the natural tendency is to hold on to the experience or try and recreate it. You can't. The point is to observe and let go.

During the process of inquiry, it's also important to be aware of what's happening in our body—this includes sensations of numbness, dullness, or tension we may feel. This means our awareness isn't solely localized in our mind but in our bodily experience as well. Again, we have no expectations about what will arise. If our shoulders or abdomen are tight or our breathing is shallow, being aware of this can provide deeper insight during the inquiry process. Our attitudes and beliefs are embedded at the muscular and even skeletal level. For instance, an attitude of fear and resistance may give us a stooped or defensive posture, which will, over time, affect the shape of our muscles and bones.

As was discussed in the preceding chapters, there's no separate self that resides in the body. We're a body-mind continuum in which changes happen at the quantum level as old beliefs and images are discarded. This doesn't mean the physical effects that developed over years because of beliefs held will vanish instantaneously from the body. There's a process by which these strongholds of ignorance are gradually dismantled, and the body starts to change to align with new understanding and feelings. Eventually and without extra effort, our thoughts, behavior, and relationships organically start to reflect this new experiential understanding. [5]

In any relationship, especially with a partner or a parent, we all know "the look." For the umpteenth time, our kid does something or forgets something, and you shoot him the look. Your eyes narrow into a stare as penetrating as the beam of a ray gun. What's expressed in your eyes is frustration, anger, or sometimes even hate.

In all likelihood, you received the look as a child, and this becomes part of the epigenetic material being passed down to the next generation. What causes the look to manifest in your life? What's the internal conversation attached to it? Using inquiry to bring this material up into your awareness without judgment initiates the process of deconstructing it.

It's important to stress the "without judgment" part. Normally, when we review some past action, we attach an internal conversation to it. "I did this because…" The "because" is a whole list of reasons that justify the action. However, in the deconstruction process, there's nothing that need be justified. There's no "because." You're solely bringing the light of awareness into an aspect of yourself that's remained hidden.

Recently, I got the look from my teenage son during a cooking class we were doing together. I did something that was upsetting to him. (I'm sure you know teenagers have a list of things their parents do that embarrass them.) Anyway, I heard this urgent whisper, "Dad, Dad," and I looked over at him. There he stood, glaring at me with the look—eyes narrowed and projecting anger and disgust. The underlying message came through loud and clear: "You're embarrassing me."

When our eyes met, I had this instantaneous experience of awareness and timelessness—of all the times I'd given him that look, the times my father had done it to me, and his father to him. By instantaneous, I mean it was outside the confines of memory. It was an immediate, direct experience of knowing.

As you begin to integrate meditation and inquiry practices into your daily life, you'll notice experiences such as this occurring, along with greater synchronicity, creativity, health, and love. It's natural for these to occur as the mind becomes more settled and less burdened with the overlay of structures. Your perception becomes different—you experience yourself in a less opaque way, but also your sense perception is much more vivid. The world you perceive just seems brighter. You're emerging into a more spacious world, so information coming through your senses is clearer and sharper. You're more aligned with life and not the image of who you think you should be.

Choosing A Simpler Object of Attention

Another approach for deconstructing our internal conversations is to simplify them. This is a contemplative practice that can be done with eyes closed or eyes open. Often our fabrications are complex and convoluted, but we can also, at times, choose which object among the many elements of an experience to pay attention to.

To start this process, we look into the reality of an emotional construct to identify the core concepts upon which it has been built. Then we are able to question the reality behind the concepts and deconstruct the pain and hurt tied up with our fixed ways of thinking. Attention placed on a particular experience within the totality of experiences is more helpful in undoing fabrication than if it's placed on others. [6]

After I wrote *Your Mitochondria—Key to Health and Longevity,* I realized there was an additional factor I hadn't considered in the book: Health and long life aren't solely based on the health of our mitochondria but also on our emotional well-being and the mental constructs under which we operate as we journey through our lives. When I had this realization, I was pulling my notes together for a second book. I started running into these abstract thought processes of determining what the new book was going to be about. Is it going to be a book on quantum physics occurring within the biology of the human body, a spiritual book, a self-help book, or what? I had to figure it out.

One day, I was riding my bike, breathing in the fresh air, listening to the birds sing, and also vaguely thinking about this question of having "to know." Just the action of exercising, breathing, and listening to Nature brought spaciousness into this process of wrestling with an abstraction.

Many times, this process of dealing with an abstraction that's taking up a lot of internal space is overlaid with a veil of concepts and images. When you create spaciousness around the abstraction, as I did on the bike ride, you can begin to see that a complex experience is actually composed of many simple factors. Cycling and breathing created spaciousness that allowed me to identify one element to pay attention to: the statement, "I need to know what I'm writing about." When I inquired into this statement, I realized that, of course, I didn't need to know right then because I was only at the stage of gathering information and making notes.

And, just like that, my mind released its hold and all that remained was me pedaling the bike, breathing, the birds chirping, and the open road in front of me.

When our actions are completely based on what we think we need from our desires and attachments, the way we perceive the world is not reliable. Many of us have experienced this in our relationships or careers. We move through a cycle in which we project happiness lying somewhere other than within ourselves. [7]

As we go through the process of deconstructive inquiry coupled with meditation to settle the mind, we come to realize that our sense of self is composed of images and masks we present to the world instead of the authentic presence of who we are. Regardless of how faithful our projected image is to our true self, it's a fake. As our practice deepens and matures, it becomes increasingly difficult to live a life without authenticity.

Take a moment and reflect on where in your life you're phony or inauthentic. Maybe you want to be perceived in a certain way in your business world. Investigate that from a place of inquiry without judgment. Do you have stories you tell yourself (internal monologues) about why you suffer? Do you need to suffer in order to feel fulfilled? These questions provide segues into determining if you're locked into a story, believing that this narrative and the fantasy of self-identity it creates are true.

We're seeking ways to recognize the falsity of our story as well as ways to deconstruct incorrect views, so a more relaxed awareness can emerge. We use meditation and inquiry practices to understand how a particular self-view has been constructed. These practices permeate consciousness. There may never be an 'ah ha' moment in which you recognize what the construction is about. Rather, the construction just becomes quieter and more in the background with the result that a significant measure of liberation and an ease of spaciousness is made available to us.

When we feel embarrassed or afraid, for example, our sense of self tends to feel more contracted, more dense, and also more separate from others and from the world. In these situations, we'll definitely be fake in our interactions. In contrast, when we feel relaxed or generous, our sense of self is more open and genuine.

Points of View and Positions

I use the terms positions, points of view, bias, assumptions, judgment, and projections in the same way. A point of view or position is automatically a restriction, and these restrictions can be emotional, physical, or mental in nature. If we look at ourselves, we become aware that we take a position on just about everything—what we're experiencing, who we're interacting with, what we're reading (you may have a position on what you're reading right now).

Here's a question – Is it possible to experience reality without taking a position about it, to be completely open to an experience and not judge it as good or bad? It's possible to perceive an experience without reacting and without running mental commentaries about it. However, to do this takes an awareness that allows us to discern that we are, in fact, judging it. How do we begin to recognize our projections, so we can ask ourselves, "OK, am I projecting/assuming/judging?"

Let's talk about some of the projections we make that are easy to identify. Tribalism is a popular term in the media today, and we can use that to identify where we have projections. Tribalism is the state of being organized in or an advocate for a particular group of people who share a common identity. Some people also use tribalism to refer to conformity, when people are loyal to their own tribe or social group and behave and think accordingly. [8]

As defined by Kanakasena Dekā, tribalism traditionally implies the possession of a strong cultural or ethnic identity that separates one member of a group from the members of other groups. Because of their geographic closeness and relatedness, members of a tribe will form a strong sense of identity. Tribal societies require ongoing customary organization, inquiry, and exchange to develop. Any group of people may feel tribally connected if they have intense feelings of common identity. [9]

So what tribes are you in? Most of us are in a political tribe. What about a nationalist tribe—my country, right or wrong? What about a religious tribe or an environmental tribe, or the LGBTQ tribe? There are many tribes people identify with, and the commonality is that strong feelings may be evoked when interacting with people outside the tribe or who have an oppositional view. The feelings evoked are the giveaway that you're engaged in projection.

I'm sure all of us know the experience of going to a holiday dinner gathering at the in-laws where both red and blue political tribes are represented. Even though you make promises to yourself that you're not going to make comments, you end up fuming about a statement so-and-so (whose political tribe isn't the same color as yours) made.

What I'm trying to get at here is, clearly, emotions are being evoked, but why do we feel so strongly about something somebody said? The "why" provides the segue into the deconstructive inquiry.

Attachment occurs in all areas in our life. One of our most deeply rooted attachments is to our self-image—both how we see ourselves and how we perceive that others see us. Our self-image is who we think we are, how we want to be seen, what we think our life should look like—which could include our home, our romantic relationships, or our career. This self-image we're attached to can be either positive or negative. If it's a positive one—and we're not seen by others in that light—this can illicit strong internal chatter and emotions. You might be attached to a self-image of being good, strong, powerful, rich, beautiful, popular, etc. Our self-image is the most superficial layer of our being, and yet, we spend much of our time being concerned about how others see and judge us. [10]

Here's an example. My friend Rosalie Chamberlain did a TED talk on "The Impact and Fear of Bias."

(https://www.youtube.com/watch?v=bcOGjvu5294)

Rosalie was raised in Georgia and grew up speaking with a southern accent. However, she's lived in different areas of the country and her accent has faded. For her TED talk on bias, she resurrected her southern accent for the first five minutes of her presentation. After five minutes, she switched back to her normal voice and asked the audience if they'd noticed any bias when she was speaking with a southern accent. Of course, many people did. This is an example of how seamlessly our biases, judgments, and projections are integrated into our daily life.

Questioning positions and points of view proceeds in the same manner as inquiry. However, these can be somewhat tricky to observe, because many times there isn't the emotional response attached to these kinds of judgments, which is the giveaway. The bias may be revealed in a simple dismissal, as happened with my friend Rosalie in her TED talk. Or we might notice we're feeling bored or impatient in a conversation or we're engaged in an internal monolog criticizing the person we're interacting with.

The positions we take automatically close us down, and this makes it difficult to experience things freshly, directly, and purely. It's important to maintain a perspective of inquiry as to why this is happening. Basically, our natural state is one of openness and a sensitivity that has no point of view and which isn't restricted by boundaries—emotional, physical, or mental. To the degree there's greater presence and spaciousness in our life and less criticism (which is based on fear, as are all other forms of judgment), our capacity for creativity, health, love, compassion, and giving is greatly increased.

How Things Are

This is a playful practice to understand to what degree the space we live in is conditioned. It's a practice of observation that can be coupled with walking meditation, which I describe later in this chapter.

We begin with the recognition that one person's reality can be, and often is, very different than what another person is experiencing. Reality—everything that exists—is all one thing. But because of our projections, beliefs, judgments, and tribalism, reality can look totally different from person to person. Additionally, each reality that we come in contact with will have its own conditioned level of truth associated with it. The conditioning is derived from both our personal projections/assumptions and our cultural conditioning. Since we're seeing a conditioned and partial view of reality, it's not a true reality.

The work we do moves us by degrees from conditioned awareness into unconditioned awareness to reveal a reality that's less structured and unencumbered by our projections, judgments, and, most importantly, is less attached to our past experience—through which we've viewed most of our life.

Let's spend some time defining conditioned and unconditioned space, which are also referred to as conceptual and nonconceptual reality. If you've ever watched parents trying to teach an infant to talk, what you observe is a lot of pointing and naming—pointing at an object and naming it. Essentially, this is what our internal world is composed of: images, names, and concepts. If this weren't so, each time we talk about something, we'd have to say a whole paragraph to describe what we're talking about. This happens in any area of study; we have to create concepts, symbols, and labels to make communication more efficient. This describes the conditioned space—the conceptual reality in which everything, including our worldview, is filtered through names and concepts.

Consider this scenario – You've been hiking up a mountain all morning and, at some point, you take a break to enjoy the vista. As you're sitting there, taking in the vast landscape, you feel relaxed as a result of the strenuous hike. In this place of relaxation and presence, you're not naming or conceptualizing. This is a taste of nonconceptual reality. It's what is, without the overlay of our past experience, our prejudices, and our mind naming everything and removing us from the immediacy of being present in the moment. Even though, in order to provide a glimpse of this, I had to use a conceptual description, it's a roadmap, not the actual experience.

Nonconceptual reality is an immediate experience, like a feeling or sensation. However, it's an awareness that isn't so overlaid with discrimination. Think about it. You wake up in the morning and discover it's an overcast day. That could be the extent of your discernment—with no internal commentary on the weather. Of course, our usual reaction is to think, "Oh, I don't like overcast days. They make me sad," and that's how your day

211

starts. This is an example of awareness overlaid with discrimination.

The following is an exercise you can do to gain a better understanding of conceptualization. During your next meditation, once you've settled and closed your eyes, note where you've placed your right hand. Your only knowledge of your hand is the sensation of it resting on the arm of the chair or on your leg. It's only our thinking that abstracts and conceptualizes a hand and a chair or leg from the intimacy and seamlessness of pure sensing. From a conceptual understanding, you think, "Pressoreceptors are sending nerve impulses from my hand to my brain." Letting go of the conceptualization, what's this experience made of? What's sensing made of?

Our attachment to the channels of our senses is a major barrier against the experience of the nonconceptual. Understanding how the senses work helps clarify the difficulty. If you have the opportunity to meditate outside, try this same exercise and notice the sounds of the birds. Notice how you locate the direction the sound is coming from and, if you're really astute, you may be able to identify the species of birds from their chirping and call up an image of the bird in your mind. However, the image in your mind isn't, of course, the real bird.

Is it the bird we hear, the air, the vibration resonating against our ear drums, or an impulse in our brain? It's all of these things. Through this process, you can understand how our past experiences, beliefs, and projections profoundly color the reality we experience. When you experience things without using your physical senses, you begin to see how your physical senses tend to prejudice you.

Of course, there's no separation between the conceptual and nonconceptual worlds, and the less we differentiate and categorize the components of the nonconceptual world, the more we rest in unstructured space, free of concepts. It's because we're in the world that we need concepts and words to communicate. However, our investment in the value of our physical senses affects our consciousness in a powerful way. We can't understand how powerful this influence is until we perceive the nonconceptual. But I want to be clear: Freedom from the senses doesn't mean we just ignore them. We have to understand that our senses don't give us the whole story.

There are times when we think we're in nonconceptual awareness and we're not. Spaciousness is a term I've used often in this book, but until you have an actual experience of it, it remains a concept in your mind. We can't know without concepts, but concepts are meant to be a roadmap. They aren't, in themselves, the territory.

Take the concept of love, which is a very charged subject. Maybe your concept of love is what you see when a mother gazes at her newborn with unconditional acceptance. However, the love we experience in the relationship with our significant other may be quite different. Here, love becomes commingled with our needs, our projections from our family of origin, and our sexuality. What emerges is a provisional love. We want to be present in our relationships, both to ourselves and to others. Being present means a true understanding emerges and we begin to work with the conditioned patterns of our personality with compassion, acceptance, forgiveness, clarity, and courage.

Presence

We've discussed presence, awareness, and mindfulness throughout this book. These terms all point to the same place—a state of less clinging in which our experience is infused with a sense of fullness. When we're present, there's no need to modify, reject, or embrace anything.

213

The exercise of presence we'll do here is one of observation. There are other presence practices that can be done in times of difficulty, stress, or suffering. Here, you're just going to notice when you're present. Of course, you're always present, in a sense, but our usual presence is filtered through our past conditioning, our habitual way of viewing things, and our blindly clinging to these ways of seeing.

The practice, then, is to notice when you're entirely in the moment—when you're not ruminating about the past or worried about your future or your self-image. Just take notice of when you're aware of being completely present. It could be after meditation, when you notice the quietness of your mind. You're not planning or lost in the past. You're totally present.

This practice opens two avenues of observation. First, you can begin to see what presence looks and feels like for you and, as your practice matures, notice how this changes. Second, our view of reality is altered when we're present. Typically, we draw on our history and beliefs about how our life has been or will be in the future. Additionally, we overlay this with hoping—hoping that something will change. Hoping causes a predictable collapse of the probability wave function. Allowing yourself to be mindful when you're resting in awareness provides a break in this causal chain. Further, when we stop allowing the constructs that our mind has forced upon us to define and restrict us, we recognize what it feels like not to be driven by our internal voices or past conditioning. We become authentic.

Here's another way to look at it. During the course of a minute, you may have a hundred or more thoughts, and those thoughts are all over the place. For example, if you're feeling depressed, every thought that emerges isn't, "I'm feeling depressed." Rather, the thought "I'm depressed" emerges, and then another thought, "I need to take a pee," follows immediately upon that, and then another, "I'm hungry," and another, "I need to get this assignment done."

These thoughts are filtered through our conditioned responses and we string all of the "I'm feeling depressed" statements together with the result that we view ourselves as having been depressed all day or all week or all our life. This is a complete fabrication, which the presence practice is designed to help you recognize.

Just so you don't think I'm referring to a state you can only achieve after years of practice, I want to point out that most of us—including you—have experienced this state. Here are some examples to help you remember when that happened:

- Consider a time when you were making love and you felt a deep, intimate connection between yourself and your partner. After making love, you felt calm, relaxed, and content. Thoughts may have arisen, but you felt no compulsion to act on them in that moment.
- Consider a time when you were working on something in which you felt truly involved—a project for school or work, or an artistic endeavor. When you were totally engrossed in the project, there was little internal chatter going on. You felt inspiration or a creative expression moving you, and time seemed to slow down.
- Consider a time when you were playing with your young child. Just the two of you were playing, and you felt relaxed and completely present to the joy and love you felt.
- After strenuous exercise, you may have noticed your internal chatter had diminished and you felt relaxed and more present to and aware of people around you. There was awareness that you were present with minimal overlay of conditioned thoughts.

Unconditioned awareness can also be tremendously healing, because the experience percolates through the layers of our habitual conditioning and changes the structure of our mind, crumbling our fixations and attachments, and, maybe, even

215

creating a radical reorientation of how we experience and understand reality. We are able to think more clearly, act more openly, and react less defensively—and hence in a better place to let go of the fears and insecurities that hold us back. [11]

At some point, we see that the practice of presence is a matter of learning to be real, learning to be authentic. We have to crave being genuine to go through the trouble and discipline of this inner work. We desire to reveal ourselves, to be authentic in our relationships, to be direct and not be fearful of seeing the truth— whether it be pleasurable, scary, or painful. To be present means we're in direct contact with our experience without defensiveness or excuses. We achieve the inner strength and foundation to be vulnerable.

Walking Meditation

This is an adaptation of traditional Buddhist walking meditation. It's more of an open, monitoring practice. Basically, we'll be more attentive to the wide range of sensations and perceptions that can be found in the present. This is a totally easy exercise. Basically, all you do is walk and breathe. How fast or slow you walk is up to you.

Unlike seated meditation, in walking meditation, we keep our eyes open, we're standing and moving, and we will more actively interact with the world. Because we're moving, you may find it easier to be mindful of the body's sensations and remain anchored in the present moment. Here are some things to notice and consider during walking meditation:

• If you're experiencing stress of whatever kind—external or internal conflicts—walking meditation can be combined with any or all of the following practices that we've already discussed:

The Essential Question

Inquiry

Choosing a Simpler Object of Attention

Points of View and Positions

• If you're feeling serene as you begin your walk, you could play around with noticing when conceptual and nonconceptual views emerge as you walk, or deliberately play with being present and then not present. Both should be light and expansive exercises.

• Stay connected to your breathing. Be sure you aren't breathing only in the upper third of your lungs. Full, deep breathing is suggested.

• Bring your awareness to your body. Notice how your body feels as you walk and try to notice as many sensations as possible within your moving body. If you notice a place of tightness, see if you can relax your body to release the tension or use your breathing to relax the tension.

• If you already walk as part of your day, incorporate walking meditation into that. If you're not currently walking, begin with a walking meditation of 15 to 20 minutes.

• Your pace should be steady and even. If your mind is agitated or you are having trouble focusing, slow down your pace and walk slowly until you can stay in the present moment with each step.

• Just as in seated meditation, distractions will arise that will catch your attention. It could be a thought or something beautiful or interesting in the environment where you're walking. Simply note these as they arise—seeing, hearing, thinking—and then drop whatever it is and continue walking. If you notice your mind wandering and getting caught up in your thoughts (or any type of mental content), bring your attention back to the physicality of your body walking and breathing.

• Of course, thoughts will arise. Some of them may be disturbing or upsetting. All that is required here is to observe your thoughts. You're just walking. You're not going anywhere. Simply be with the process of walking and breathing.

• If strong feelings arise and keep your mind busy, it's OK to let yourself get lost in those thoughts. It can be helpful to deepen your breathing. When the thoughts are no longer compelling, you return to the rhythm of walking, breathing, and presence. There's nothing we need to do during walking meditation except be present. Our true home resides in the present moment.

• The ability to focus, which walking meditation helps to develop, can be carried into our daily life as well as into our seated practice, where there are less sensory stimuli. This is a powerful tool. During times when we're feeling strong emotion or stress, we may find that it easier to relax and focus in walking meditation than while sitting. Additionally, walking, especially if done outdoors, as an exercise has health and well-being benefits.

Several times in this book, I've alluded to the fact that, as you do this work, you begin to experience your life as a meditation. All this means is we bring mindfulness to everything we do— formal meditation, walking meditation, taking out the garbage, doing our work. We think of all activities in our life as a type of meditation. Playing-with-our-children-meditation, doing-the-laundry-meditation, calming-down-a friend-meditation, etc.

The consciousness that looks back at you in the mirror every morning is the same consciousness that looked back at you as a child. The only change has been the aging of our bodies. Our consciousness knows only presence. And so, in walking meditation, we stand up from the meditative repose and walk through our life with awareness and presence.

Back Where We Started From

I mentioned that when I first started gathering information for this book, I had these abstract thoughts telling me I needed to know what I was writing about. Those thoughts were stressful for me. In other words, I suffered some.

Basically, *my position* (emphasis mine) was that it was taking me too long to write. I was under no deadline to finish by a certain time. This was an internal pressure that I put on myself. A week would go by, and I'd feel no passion to write. During this time, I was doing the inquiry practices and observing (with compassion) this demand I was making on myself. My creative process didn't look like I thought it should look nor was it happening as fast as I wanted. Our willfulness causes us suffering, and it takes strength and compassion toward oneself to take a deep breath and allow the unexpected to emerge.

We all have places in ourselves that cause us to struggle and suffer. My suffering is different than your suffering, and it's also the same. A transparency emerges that dismantles a fundamental misconception—a misconception based on hope and wishing. We look outside of ourselves and wish for more money, a better relationship, or "to be a star" with the false belief that our suffering will end. Do you really think that if you were someone else your suffering would disappear? Do you think media stars don't have suffering in their life?

Dismantling these image and beliefs allows us to begin to live our life fully and authentically without pretense and without hope. As we live our lives, we say to ourselves, "I choose to be present in my life, which includes those times I may suffer."

As we do this work, our capacity for compassion toward ourselves and all beings greatly increases. This means we can accept those times when we suffer and not feel we have to come up with a story to explain the suffering or figure out how to avoid it. Our journey into emptiness—in both the quantum and Buddhist views—brings us an expanded capacity to express loving-kindness, compassion, generosity, and deep caring for the world around us.

References:

1. Burbea, Rob. Seeing That Frees: Meditations on Emptiness and Dependent Arising (Kindle Locations 2262-2265). Hermes Amāra. Kindle Edition.
2. Almaas, A. H. (2008). The Unfolding Now: Realizing Your True Nature Through the Practice of Presence. (p. 121) Boston, Mass: Shambhala.
3. Katie, Byron. Loving What Is: Four Questions That Can Change Your Life (p. 3). Potter/TenSpeed/Harmony. Kindle Edition.
4. Almaas, A.H. Runaway Realization (Kindle Locations 233) Shambhala. Kindle Edition.
5. Ibid p. 134
6. Burbea, Rob. Seeing That Frees: Meditations on Emptiness and Dependent Arising (Kindle Locations 1839-1842). Hermes Amāra. Kindle Edition.
7. Fenner, Ph.D., Peter. Radiant Mind (p. 137). Sounds True. Kindle Edition.
8. http://oxforddictionaries.com/definition/english/tribalism?q=tribalism
9. Kanakasena Dekā; Kanakasena Ḍekā (1993). Assam's Crisis: Myth & Reality. Mittal Publications. pp. 90. ISBN 978-81-7099-473-2.
10. Almaas, A. H. (2000). *Diamond Heart: Book Four: Indestructible Innocence.* (p. 173) Boston, Mass: Shambhala Publications.
11. Fenner, Ph.D., Peter. Radiant Mind (p. 8). Sounds True. Kindle Edition.

Chapter 10
The Mystery

"With compassion, one has all the teachings, Without compassion, one has none of them. Even those who meditate on emptiness need compassion as its essence."

-Matthieu Ricard, trans.,The Life of Shabkar: The Autobiography of a Tibetan Yogi, 2001

During the course of our investigation, we've shown the impact that our thoughts have on our life. Specifically, the nature of our reality is informed by our every act, every thought, every intention, and every perception. Each of these has an immediate impact, however unimaginably tiny, upon the quantum ground of reality.

In the first chapter, I introduced the Chinese medicine concept of the knotty problem. As you recall, this concept was used to describe three knotty problems I encountered when writing this book:

- my dilemma in accounting for the energy needed to drive the functions of vision and memory
- the implications of the collapse of the quantum wave function due to the influence of the observer
- how our thinking (consciousness) affects our health and life

The resolution of these problems has taken us on a journey of questioning some fundamental scientific worldviews and into the realms of cellular biology, quantum physics, and Buddhist philosophy.

Changing Our Worldview

When I began this exploration, I was very sure of the science of cellular biology and the cell's role in the energy production that controls our health and longevity. However, as my investigations progressed, my thinking evolved as some of my own blinders regarding how I viewed the world were removed.

To learn anything, it's necessary to have the courage to accept that what we think we know—including our most rooted convictions—may be wrong. A different worldview began to emerge for me, one that demonstrated the interrelationship and interdependence of all sentient beings on our planet. What started out as an investigation into energy flow within the body morphed into revealing how our beliefs influence not only our behavior, but how our lives—including our health, longevity, and creativity—unfold.

What this book identifies is a transformative process accomplished by the mind acting upon its own internal processes. The mind is seen as a quantum process creating the inner experience of awareness. The inner experience of awareness is a burst of luminosity, but, surrounding that insight, is a sea of mystery. Within the mystery, everything exists in an interconnected web of relationship.

The Transformative Process

The foundational parts of this web are the many small pieces of information. From emptiness, information spontaneously emerges. It takes time to process, synthesize, and observe this information and then construct the reality around us. We can spontaneously discover new bits of information through our lives and use them to further improve our understanding of reality. This spontaneous emergence is the collapse of wave function. [1]

In Buddhist philosophy, the sea of mystery is the nondual ground of experience, which is the realization that there's basically only aware presence. Two approaches—Buddhism and quantum science—point to the same view of reality—a reality in which awareness emerges from quantum emptiness.

There are a couple of other insights I want to touch on to fully identify how this transformative process unfolds in our life. Fully integrating these insights helps to shift our priorities to the awakening of presence in each moment—not in some imagined future—which yields genuine happiness and freedom.

Back in the 1980s, my first wife and I lived in Santa Rosa, California. Our home had a view of the foothills and, during the warm months, fog would roll in every evening to envelope the foothills as the cool air from the Pacific Ocean met the warm air over the land. One late afternoon, we were lying in bed reading and occasionally noticing the fog as it rolled in. At some point, we started talking about money. That conversation quickly devolved into an argument.

In counseling, there's a term called "marital sadism," which means each partner knows the other's sensitive buttons and, at times, will deliberately provoke the other by pushing those buttons—kind of like throwing little grenades at each other. The grenades were flying during our argument.

Anyway, there we were, totally caught up in our defenses and projections, and suddenly there was a sound of glass breaking. Something invisible flew into the room and struck both of us. In that moment, we had a mysterious and profound experience. We observed a luminosity in the room, and all the objects appeared vibrant and alive with color.

Neither of us could remember what we were arguing about. All we were aware of was a deep sense of love and compassion between us. As I looked at her, I felt no separation—just radiance and love. Then a sense of humorous wisdom arose as we looked at each other. We both started laughing, which morphed into tears of joy. Just the thought of how deadly serious we'd been moments before was cracking us up. Eventually, we ended up making love. And, later when we investigated, we found there were no broken windows or glass anywhere in the house.

At the time this occurred, I wasn't meditating, nor had I done any personal work on myself. It was only years later that I had some insight into what had happened to us. What had occurred was nothing short of a spontaneous awakening into nondual awareness. There's substantial literature on these types of experiences happening to people—both meditators and non-meditators.

Our Beliefs Create our Experience—and Our Life

From what we've discussed in the preceding chapters, that experience could be interpreted as follows:

The first condition we can point to is our belief that our being resides in, is made of, and is limited to our body and mind. We believe our self resides within the body and mind and that everyone and everything else resides outside. This is the fundamental presumption of our entire culture: experience is divided into two parts—a separate, interior self that knows, feels, and perceives; and separate, exterior objects, others, or phenomena that are known, felt, or perceived.

Emptiness is the understanding that dispels this illusion of separateness. Both from the view of quantum physics and Buddhist meditation traditions, emptiness is understood to mean everything is interrelated and interdependent. We have relationships with absolutely everything—whether we realize it or not. No one and nothing exists in isolation or separation.

This first condition also speaks directly to my wife and my experience of "something" coming from outside and striking us. From the perspective of the separate self, that was the only way we could process the experience.

A second condition deals with releasing tension in the body. Our belief of being separate keeps our bodies in a constant state of low-grade tension—a wariness that something "outside" ourselves may cause us harm. In the case of my wife and me, the argument we were having contributed another, significant layer of tension in both of us.

However, we've all become so accustomed to this state of tension and contraction that it doesn't even register with us. It just seems normal. Like a person who has walked around with clenched fists for so long that they're no longer aware that they're constantly on the defensive, our body and mind have been permeated by tension and contraction generated by our sense of being a separate and hidden self for so long that we're not aware of it.

Consider what happens when there's an instantaneous experience of emptiness. I don't mean an intellectual understanding of it. I mean a full body-and-mind awareness of it. Our muscles immediately release and relax. Having this direct knowing that we're not separate, not alone, allows us to relax. This sensation of relaxing is how we become aware of being struck.

Regarding the breaking-of-the-glass experience my wife and I shared, all of our beliefs, perceptions about life, projections, and biases acted like an opaque barrier obscuring our direct knowing of the unlimited nature of our self and of life. It's a shattering experience to have that which has obscured our vision for so long be removed.

When we're present in our life, we feel a sense of immediacy, of fullness, in every experience. This sense pervades and fills our consciousness with the awareness of our interconnectedness and interdependence with everything. Loving kindness, compassion, generosity, and deep care for the world open naturally in the heart as a consequence. Experiencing emptiness opens us to love.

This is what happened to my wife and me, but, at the time, we were confused and didn't know how to interpret what we experienced. Over time, the experience began to fade, and our old conditioning and beliefs reappeared—seeking happiness, peace, and love by accumulating objects, relationships, and stimulation. However, what *did* remain for me was a deep curiosity: "What was *that*?"

And, like the prodigal son, I ventured to far-off places in search of an answer—only to eventually return to myself.

Beware "The Glamors"

An awakening coupled with other abilities may occur as your practice and inquiry develop. I call these abilities the glamors, and I'll explain to you shortly why I call them that. However, there's another name for these abilities—*siddhis*. *Siddhi* is a Sanskrit term meaning "attainment" or "perfection" that results from meditative practice.

Many variations of the *siddhis* are described in the Buddhist tradition. Today, we associate most of them with psychic or "psi" phenomena. They include hands-on healing, telepathy (mind-to-mind communication), clairvoyance (gaining information about distant or hidden objects beyond the reach of the ordinary senses), precognition (clairvoyance through time), and psychokinesis—PK (direct influence over matter by the mind). [2]

Dean Radin of the Institute of Noetic Sciences surveyed over a thousand meditators, which was part of an advanced meditation research initiative. The survey found that three out of four meditators reported increases in synchronicities in their life as a result of their practice. Nearly half reported sensing "non-physical entities," and a third reported psi experiences such as clairvoyance or telepathy. This means that exceptional experiences aren't so exceptional after all for meditators. These findings warrant closer study of these experiences under more controlled conditions. [3]

If you consider what's happening as your meditative experience deepens, *siddhis* aren't that unusual, just as Radin found. There's a simple explanation: The meditative experience is one of emptiness and presence, which is a result of letting go of limiting beliefs and projections about our life. It's as if we've been viewing our life through a dirty window that we've been gradually cleaning through our meditative practice. We realize this window is part of a door we can walk through into the clear, unobstructed day. As we become more connected with our authentic self and those around us, we have access to more immediate, unfiltered information including *siddhis*.

To frame this from a quantum viewpoint, as our thinking becomes less limited by ingrained, repetitive thought patterns, more possibilities for the collapse of the wave function open up. Here are some of the simpler ways this may show up in your life:

• You begin to notice a natural flow in your life that includes increasing numbers of synchronicities—you think about something and it shows up the next day.

• You have greater empathy for people you come in contact with, which allows you to give them a word, phrase, or touch that has significant meaning for that person.

• Your dreams begin to have meaning in your everyday life.

• Your trust in your insights and intuition increases, allowing for greater creativity in your life.

So, here's where the glamors come in. These openings can be seductive, and it's easy to start thinking of yourself as special: *"I have this special skill."* Of course, you *are* special, but it's not that "I"-centered kind of special. It's a specialness that arises from your understanding of interrelatedness and interdependence. Essentially, it's your openness that makes you special. The "I"-centered sense of being special closes you off and limits you.

Let me give you an example so you can see how this might play out. Let's say you recognize that you have healing abilities. You're empathic to people's feelings, and you can sense if they have a disease process occurring. When you initially become aware of this, you offer healing to your friends and family in the form of touch. They start feeling better or experience some deep emotional shift. Your friends tell their friends, and soon people are calling you for healings. This is where the test comes up: Is this the "I" doing the healing or is this gift of healing the expression of your greater awareness, openness, and presence? It takes effort not to be seduced by the glamors and commit to constantly returning to your meditative practice.

Social Activism

In the last chapter, we discussed points of view, tribalism, and how the positions we take and the tribes we belong to can create personal suffering for us and limit our creativity. Inquiry was suggested as an approach to begin to observe when we're taking a position and whether misconceptions and beliefs are used to justify it.

This doesn't mean you move through the world with no grounding or feelings. It's not like you're on a remote mountaintop meditating with no distraction or interaction but rather living your life while actively engaged in the world. This means you may belong to a tribe that you feel impassioned about, and strong feelings will come up.

Ongoing practice naturally leads to a deeper sense of compassion, generosity, and love resulting from a lessening of our identification as a separate self and the realization of our connectedness with everything. The issue then becomes that it's not enough just to be content with developing love and compassion as unexpressed qualities. We also have to be able to transform these inner states into practical actions that help bring real relief to the suffering of other living beings.

The way we each identify with "I," "me," and "myself" is subtle and usually hidden from our awareness. We may tie our identity with our body, feelings, and thoughts; we identify with images, patterns, roles, and archetypes. When we hold onto these false identities, our lives become devoted to protecting and defending them, and then striving to fulfill what's limited or deficient in them, and fearing their loss. If we're completely identified with these false selves, there's little opportunity for meaningful investigation to occur. [3]

The Four Noble Truths invite us to examine how we create our own suffering. As we explore this in ourselves, we quite naturally begin to recognize the suffering occurring around us, including that arising from political, social, and economic causes. Such insight can result in greater political engagement or social activism, which can lead to a deepening sense of gratitude for our life, and increasing awareness of how we affect one another. This gratitude isn't simply an emotion but a way of being. Expressing it often occurs as generosity. The impulse of generosity is to look for ways to be helpful and of service. This is a natural, organic outcome of long-term practice.

As our practice progresses, we become more present and comfortable in our life. We begin to move in and out of the realization that there's only presence to what is, and everything that exists resides in that presence. Reality is a unified field of awareness, but we're in the habit of differentiating it into separate pieces because of our (mis)perceptions.

Social activism gives us an avenue to explore this, and we can use inquiry to discover why we feel impassioned to be politically or socially active. Such inquiry may reveal we're involved because we want to achieve something, or it might reveal that our motivation is to help alleviate suffering, or protect the environment. However, this can propel us into envisioning a future orientation in which we lose our sense of the here and now. There will always be tension between seeking to resolve a social injustice—which is viewed as a goal in the future—and acting out of an emptiness in the moment in which we have nothing to gain, nothing to lose, and the intention/action is complete in itself. We're not attached to the outcome.

Thinking of interrelationship and interdependence within Buddhist ideology can level the social hierarchy when we think about an individual and how they are connected to their community. The community is everyone and everything, and the social implication of this viewpoint is, of course, powerful. My neighbor's poverty becomes my poverty; his tragedy, my tragedy. And, when combined with active engagement as modeled by the bodhisattva ideal—in which personal benefit is achieved by helping others—we now have a fundamental reason for our social action.

We, ourselves, have been involved in, or the media has exposed us to, situations in which political or social groups with different viewpoints come together. Sometimes these groups end up shouting at each other—or worse—and there's no way for communication to occur. As part of our ongoing practice, we cultivate the habit of asking questions as opposed to digging in our heels and insisting on our way or the highway. We carry out this questioning internally as a way to understand our self and our reactions. This practice of asking questions rather than making demands or accusations also works well in political or social activism. Engaging in politics through asking questions and exploring how it is affecting our interconnected community is a very different approach than focusing on only defending our position or assumptions.

Social activism involves engagement with many different types of egos and ego-based institutions. Our work is about staying present to allow the outflow of generosity, compassion, and service. This is a practice of the heart, because it takes strength and fearlessness to not flee from suffering into anger, self-righteousness, or numbness but rather keep returning to presence and do the courageous work of the heart. (See the essay on Hell Realms in the Appendices)

It is difficult work to get tossed back and forth between your quiet, spacious world and the active, lively world out there, and it may take time until it doesn't feel like you're being tossed anymore. When you find the stable place in your being that contains both the stillness and the activity, there will be the generous outpouring of your heart to help, no matter what conditions surround you. Social activism is where consciousness plus commitment come together to create change.

For those who feel inspired toward social activism, Appendix 4 describes in depth some of the man-made hell realms we've created on this planet that we have the power to dismantle.

Waking, Dreaming, Sleeping, and Death

In earlier chapters, we discussed the "gaps" in scientific explanations, particularly in the context of energy flow within the body. The accepted worldview has been that the energy to drive all the physiological and neurological processes within the body is accounted for by chemical interactions. As we found out, this isn't the case.

In this last chapter, I want to discuss another scientific gap, which has to do with sleep. Sleep has been described as a biological process occurring in the brain as a result of the release of neurotransmitters such as GABA, melatonin, and adenosine synchronized with the body's circadian rhythm. This all sounds reasonable. However, the National Institute of Neurological Disorders and Stroke adds this to its explanation of the phenomenon of sleep: "Everyone needs sleep, but its biological purpose remains a mystery. Sleep affects almost every type of tissue and system in the body—from the brain, heart, and lungs to metabolism, immune function, mood, and disease resistance. Research shows that a chronic lack of sleep, or poor-quality sleep, increases the risk of disorders including high blood pressure, cardiovascular disease, diabetes, depression, and obesity." [4]

It's not clear why we sleep, or the mechanisms involved in causing us to sleep. This leads us directly into one of our most tightly held beliefs. First, consider what happens when you go to sleep. You're lying all comfy in your bed, maybe thinking about some of the day's activities, and then boom...you're out. It's as if someone turned off a switch in your head. The French have a term for this—*la petite mort* (the little death). In modern usage, this phrase means "a state or event resembling or prefiguring death; a weakening or loss of consciousness, specifically in sleep or during an orgasm." [5]

So, we could say that every night we experience a little death, but then we're back the next day—which isn't too far off the mark of where we're going in this discussion.

This loss of consciousness can be easily understood in terms of what happens physiologically and psychologically during an orgasm, which requires us to surrender, to let down our guard as well as our projections and beliefs. We surrender to the sensations that overtake our body. We release the "I" consciousness—that separate identity we rigidly hold on to—

and surrender to the universal consciousness that permeates everything.

If we think about this, we realize there are aspects of ourselves that can't be explained merely by considering ourselves as physical organisms. How can this body, this physical thing, have dreams at night—dreams that look as real as our waking reality? When we move around in our dreams and talk to people, it seems real. We experience strong emotions, and everything is as real as it is when we're awake. How does that happen? How can we, during sleep, experience a whole universe exactly as real as our waking world? But, when we wake up, we say, "Oh, that was just a dream. This is real life." How do we know?

If we are able to live in a dream in which everything feels real, doesn't it make sense that we have the ability to create the life we're living right now? [6]

Most of us accept a set of beliefs or views as unquestionably self-evident. We invest a sort of solidity and stability into what we believe are "facts." In other words, we regard these views and beliefs as inherently existent. Our belief in our own mortality is one of those bedrock beliefs and is the fundamental assumption upon which most other beliefs and feelings—and, subsequently, our activities and relationships—are based. And, as it happens, holding to such beliefs is the source of most of our suffering. The fear of our disappearance or death is, in fact, the primary emotion behind associating our self with our body or mind.

We take for granted that we're born, we age, we grow old, and we die. Let's examine this "fact" in the context of what we've learned about the collapse of the wave function, the role of the observer (which is us), and the Buddhist concept of emptiness.

Throughout this book, I've demonstrated how our beliefs, misconceptions, and past traumas influence and shape our life.

233

Essentially, what you think is what you live—you are what you think—which, from the quantum view, represents the collapse of the wave function caused by you, the observer.

Now I'm going to push the envelope a bit further by stating that all beings are dreaming within the dream, and the nature of our dreaming determines the future course of the dream. For this reason, it's vital that we find a way to control our waking dream. Life is dreamlike—and, therefore, ultimately unreal. It takes place within the field of awareness-consciousness—the wave function.

If the word "dream" seems too radical to you as a definition of our life, substitute the word "reality." When we're in a waking dream/reality, our beliefs and misconceptions create a world with which we interact—fully believing it's real.

We only need to watch TV or a movie to see the content of the dreaming we're creating—wars, planetary disasters, and violence; dystopic views of sexuality and relationships; and striving to accumulate wealth and power—which keep us trapped in a materialistic metaphor. Of course, there are also extraordinary movies and other forms of art that depict the magnificence of the human spirit. All of these are extensions of our dreaming.

The terms "unborn" and "undying" appear in the Perfection of Wisdom sutras that are part of Mahayana Buddhism. Without going into great detail, "unborn" is a synonym for emptiness or "lacking inherent existence." It follows that if nothing is born, nothing dies. In the context of emptiness—both from the quantum view and the Buddhist view—this is understood to mean that because everything is interrelated and interdependent, there's no individual entity to be born or to die.

This idea is in direct contradiction to our accepted worldview of ourselves, which is:

- *Our* consciousness is a byproduct of *our* (individual, separate) brain.
- Our consciousness only exists as long as our physical body exists
- My body defines "me" and everything outside my body defines other— "not me."
- The "I" defined by my body lives and dies separate from everything else.

Take a moment and reflect on some past experience that was significant for you. The "I" you were then is the same "I," the same self, as you are now. Your body may have aged, but the self that knows and experiences has not.

To be more specific, every morning you get up and brush your teeth in front of a mirror. As you're brushing, you may be having a mental conversation with yourself about what you'll do that day, your appearance as it's reflected back to you in the mirror, and so on. The question then is, is the self you're conversing with aware of its inherent, unchanging nature? From childhood to now, there's only been one aware presence gazing back at you from the mirror. Thoughts, feelings, sensations, images, memories, and perceptions change, but the self that knows or experiences them does not.

This chapter is titled "The Mystery," and here it is: We move in and out of believing we're separate and not separate. "Not separate" here refers to an experience of unconditioned awareness, aware presence, emptiness, of being unborn and undying. Here I deliberately contrast *believing* you're separate with *knowing* you're present and never have been separate.

Maintaining this awareness can be a struggle. Throughout this book, I've pointed out little places in our life where knowing permeates our consciousness. After meditation, we may notice a quiet presence. After making love, presence may emerge. Often when we're playing with our child, all else falls away and only presence remains. When we're hiking or biking, we're breathing, our thinking slows, and presence emerges. And when we fall asleep, we dream, and presence emerges.

Living in Aware Presence

The experience of aware presence is always available to us. No preparation is necessary. All we have to do is just let go of our mental fabrications rather than trying to achieve some imagined higher spiritual state. You can't "create" an experience of aware presence, but we can stop creating the obstructions that inhibit the experience. We do our contemplative practice and observe and inquire into our beliefs—not for the purpose of gaining but to lose and let go of mental habits and conditioning that create obstructions to being fully present in our life.

Our fear of death lies at the heart of our belief in the separate self that our thinking imagines us to be. This belief creates a tremendous burden in our lives, but when we experience moments of aware presence, that burden is lifted, and we lose our fear of death. It's difficult to put into words an experience of losing our fear of death, and this is why I originally titled this book, *That Which Cannot Be Named.* Unfortunately, several people told me, "It sounds too much like a *Harry Potter* title," so I changed it.

So, we lose our fear of death. What does that mean? We've defined emptiness as the interrelated and interconnected nature of everything. At an intellectual level, we understand this claim as, "Of course, I acknowledge that the air I breathe has been breathed by millions of people, and the sunlight that warms me nourishes all life on the planet. But, obviously, I'm still separate."

It isn't too difficult for us to acknowledge we're a tiny part of a vast something, yet we perceive ourselves as physically separate: *I'm here, sitting in my chair, and you're there, sitting in your chair.* However, emptiness and aware presence interpenetrate the parts and pieces of everything. It's understood not only from a Buddhist perspective but from the experiences of people of all faiths over the centuries that a subtle, nonconceptual, unbounded consciousness forms the essence of one's own being and of all life. This is a mutual transparency of self and other in which everything—including our own being—is revealed to comprise a unified, vast expanse of consciousness. This aware-presence consciousness knows itself; therefore, it's said to be unborn and undying.

This level of consciousness is the source of all higher qualities of being. Compassion, insight, joy, and strength manifest spontaneously when we realize this. We experience all beings, including our planet, from an open-ended and fully encompassing state of compassion.

It's not that easy to transition from a structured reality to an unstructured reality, but this is the mystery we participate in, the mystery of existence. Your two choices are (and either choice is OK) to stay comfortable in your current worldview or to be open, relaxed, and curious about what may be unfolding right in front of your eyes—a true Greek drama in which you're the writer, producer, director, and lead actor/actress.

So, there's the mystery of existence and there's our participation in this mystery. There are two ways we can participate—either as a lonely and isolated, separate self, or as a dancer and explorer in our own lives. The choice is all yours. Our reality is the shared reality of everyone—of all sentient beings, of all that exists.

One Last Knotty Problem

I want to end this book with a final knotty problem for you to consider. Our investigation has examined how our thinking, our beliefs, misconceptions, biases, and unchallenged allegiance to our worldview creates our reality and affects our health, longevity, creativity, and ability to be fully present in our life.

Although we may vigorously maintain that external circumstances are the cause of our current life situation, it takes very little self-reflection to see the fallacy of this view.

Self-reflection—coupled with meditation—is the primary approach suggested throughout this book as a way to deconstruct the thought patterns and beliefs that constrict us. Integrating these insights into our everyday life helps shift priorities from the pursuit of more money, more social status, and bigger homes to the pursuit of genuine happiness and freedom. A radical decline in mean-spirited internal dialogues, delusions, envy, and anger occurs when we gain insight into the profound interdependence of all beings, and our love and compassion burst forth.

At the individual level, a simple takeaway is: Our thoughts have power. They create circumstances in which we live in love and compassion or in difficulty, and our thoughts alone motivate us to hurt or help others.

Herein lies the crux of the final knotty problem. At the individual level, we can understand how our conditioned self creates much of our suffering. However, if we remove our attention from our self and look at the world, the sources of suffering become much more complex and unclear. For example, we can see how craving for more money and power creates giant inequalities in the world that drive suffering, but how does that logic apply in the case of a child born with birth defects or the deaths of some 1.3 million people in 2016 from tuberculosis? [6] Tuberculosis, which is caused by the bacterium *Mycobacterium tuberculosis*, has been around for millennia, and yet millions of people still die from it each year.

We could describe the path toward understanding this knotty problem in this way: Our initial desire is to understand ourselves, alleviate our suffering, and have a fuller life. This takes us on an initial journey of increasingly greater insight into our ordinary experiences. This becomes our meditative practice, which is coupled with inquiry into all aspects of our daily life.

As our practice deepens, we come to recognize the relationship of ordinary experience to deeper levels of reality—how our experience reflects emptiness—that which is interdependent and interconnected. At this stage, our social awareness opens, and we feel a desire to help others and the planet. Helping manifests in many different forms. It could involve driving our elderly neighbor to the grocery store, donating money, or engaging in social activism. As greater presence emerges in our life, there's a corresponding emergence of compassion—both for our self and for the world at large. That compassion translates into wanting to alleviate suffering however we can. Eventually, we're able to see how our individual experience is nothing but aware presence. The separate "I' drops away and there are times when we rest in this presence—the oneness that is nondual reality.

Although I refer to these as stages, they're not really stages on a road to someplace. Fundamentally, there's nowhere to go. It's our commitment to practice that allows deeper and deeper levels of reality to open—and this process is infinite. Each time we reach one level, a deeper level of reality opens that allows us different realizations. Reality is bigger than the perception of the individual. Reality is an immensity that's constantly manifesting and revealing its possibilities. [7]

And so, it's from this perspective that we can resolve the knotty problem of the occurrence of birth defects, deaths from treatable diseases, and other suffering that is difficult to understand and accept from our conditioned worldview. As our practice deepens and aware presence begins to permeate our life, realizations and understanding emerge.

As more people become aware of this conscious ability to reside in an awareness that has no boundaries in space-time, we can't help but reach a point of awareness in which humanity realizes its highest potential. We humans are on the pioneering edge of our greatest evolutionary change to date, but many of us are oblivious or unaware of this, or are confused by our attempts to understand ourselves. However, understand ourselves we must. The world looks messy now, but that's what change looks like. Millions of people all over the planet are doing some form of practice. We practice because we want to live fully, we want to be free, we want to discover the mysteries of existence, we want to fulfill our life's purpose. We can see our motivation in many ways. It's a part of a natural process that people are trying to change the thought-forms that drive our materialistic, aggressive behavior and create so much suffering.

The environmental problems that endanger our world transcend the barriers of race, culture, or religion. The industrial toxins, radioactive waste, and greenhouse gases responsible for global warming ignore national borders. These and other problems—poverty, war, famine—that threaten humanity can be solved if we realize we're all interdependent and our interests and happiness are inextricably bound up with those of all other beings.

I want to thank you for taking the journey of reading this book. My prayer is that something has been stirred in you—a longing or an intuition that's been awakened in your mindstream or as a direct, immediate understanding that allows you to see the fallacy of ourselves as separate and recognize the distortions through which we've viewed the world. Aware presence is and has always been our true nature.

So, with my deep love for The Mystery, acknowledgment of aware presence, and devotion to helping all beings to be free from suffering, I offer this book.

References:

1. Vedral, Vlatko. Decoding Reality: The Universe as Quantum Information (Oxford Landmark Science) (p. 218). OUP Oxford. Kindle Edition.
2. Radin, D. (2015). Meditation and the Nonlocal Mind. EXPLORE: The Journal of Science and Healing, 11(2), 82–84. https://doi.org/10.1016/j.explore.2014.12.011
3. Kornfield, J. (n.d.). No Self or True Self? - Identity and Selflessness in Buddhism. Retrieved from https://tricycle.org/magazine/no-self-or-true-self/ Brain Basics: Understanding Sleep. (n.d.). Retrieved from https://www.ninds.nih.gov/Disorders/Patient-Caregiver-Education/Understanding-Sleep
4. Oxford English Dictionary (Third ed.). Oxford University Press. 2005. Retrieved 21 August 2015.
5. Almaas, A.H. Diamond Heart: Book Five, Shambhala Publications, 2011, p. 200.
6. Global tuberculosis report. World Health Organization. Retrieved 2017-11-09.
7. Almaas, A.H. Diamond Heart: Book Five, Shambhala Publications, 2011, p. 116.

Appendix 1: Resources

The first two resources below may be helpful for those who have no experience with meditation or anyone who would like assistance in settling their mind. The next two resources are for those who want a more formalized approach for doing inquiry into their inner world in a group setting.

Muse

http://www.choosemuse.com/

Muse is a described as a "brain-sensing headband" used to provide feedback on the quality of the user's meditation. The headband does this by translating brain signals into the sounds of wind. When the mind is calm and settled, the sound is like that of a gentle breeze, but if the mind is agitated, the sound is of fiercely blowing wind. The vendor of Muse offers a tutorial on how to adjust the headband to assure brain signals are read correctly.

The device self-calibrates prior to each session by taking a snapshot of the wearer's brain in a natural state and using this as a reference for assessing brain signals. After each session, graphs and charts are generated to track progress over time—from as little as a few seconds to an entire session to months. These results are saved in a private account. Muse also gives the wearer points, goals, challenges, and bonuses to enhance motivation.

Muse is connected to an app on a mobile device via Bluetooth. The intention of Muse is to allow the user to improve their meditation, which, in turn, will reduce stress, depression, and other negative mental states and lead to greater calm and equanimity.

Another product similar to Muse is:

Emotiv

https://www.emotiv.com/

Emotiv is similar to Muse but has two different types of hardware and software and wider applications including performance and wellness as well as brain research and education. The two types of Emotiv hardware, Insight and Epic+, are worn on the head like headphones. Insight, which is the less bulky device, is described as "a prosumer, five-channel, mobile EEG meant to be used by individuals seeking better understanding of their brains and mental states." Epic+ is a high-resolution, 14-channel, mobile EEG meant for "contextualized, scientific, research-grade results."

Both devices track facial expressions and a variety of emotional states—excitement, frustration, stress, meditation, relaxation, interest, and focus.

EmotivePRO is the software that operates on Insight and Epic+ headsets and is described as "an integrative software solution for neuroscience research and education." There's a companion app, MYEmotiv, to the Emotiv Insight and Epic+ wearable EEG headsets that graphically presents and saves brain activity, emotional metrics and activity patterns, and recommends activities to improve daily function and manage stress.

Diamond Approach

https://www.diamondapproach.org/

The Diamond Approach is described by its developer as "a dynamic, evolving teaching that leads to openness, freedom, and realization of the many dimensions of our human potential—especially the amazing secrets of our spiritual nature." The Diamond Heart website states there are no beliefs to accept or ideology to embrace. The student only needs a sincere desire to know what is true about themselves.

The central practice of inquiry in the Diamond Approach engages and explores the student's inner world. Along with verbal exploration, the teaching uses movement practices and breath work to engage the wisdom of the body. The teachings are offered in "an organic, deepening sequence" in a group setting to allow students to contact their inner guidance.

Developed by Hameed Ali, founder of The Ridhwan School, the Diamond Approach combines time-honored, spiritual practices with modern psychological understanding "to penetrate obscurations to your inner richness and luminous depth."

The Diamond Approach is taught in seminars, workshops, public talks, etc. all over the world. The Ridhwan School exists in many locations on multiple continents, and new groups form if sufficient interest exits. There are also online programs.

Radiant Mind

http://www.radiantmind.net/

The Radiant Mind organization offers programs inspired by the Mahayana Buddhist traditions of Zen, Dzogchen, Mahamudra, and Madhyamaka. These programs use the realization of nondual awareness as the source for authentic intimacy, healing, and inner peace.

As described on their website, "Radiant mind arises when unconditioned awareness radiates through the totality of our conditioned existence. When we live in radiant mind, we experience ourselves as a unique human being while at the same time resting in a unified expanse of centerless and boundless awareness. This state is called liberation, Buddha nature, egolessness, pure presence, nondual wisdom, our natural condition, and effortless being."

Appendix 2: Tsa Lung Meditation

Introduction

I recognize that some people reading this book may be dealing with serious health concerns. If you are, then this section would be a good consideration. The practice is useful for improving overall health.

In reading this section I would encourage you to bring awareness to the practice outlined in this book. This means as you read this section, or do the exercise, be aware of judgment, beliefs, statements that would say this cannot possibly help me.

The question raised here is what do you have to lose? All that is being asked of you is to sit quietly and breathe. Who knows something totally spontaneous may emerge or, if not, then you have just taken the time to add more oxygen to your body which in and of it itself is healthy.

The Powerful Practice of Tsa Lung Meditation—The Effect of Focus and Intentional Breathing on Health and Longevity

The Tibetan Buddhist lama Phakyab Rinpoche immigrated to the United States in 2003 as a 37-year-old refugee. When he arrived, he was suffering from diabetes and Pott's Disease, a form of tuberculosis that occurs outside the lungs. He had advanced gangrene in his right leg and foot. The New York medical community agreed that the only way to save Phakyab Rinpoche's life was to amputate his leg.

Rinpoche conferred with the Dalai Lama, who advised him to do Tsa Lung meditation to heal himself and then teach others the value of this ancient tradition.

After meditating for nine months—while taking no medication and eating an ordinary diet—Phakyab Rinpoche's leg was much improved. At ten months, he could walk with crutches, and at

247

one year, his leg was fully functional. He, and the Dalai Lama, attributed his recovery to his practice of Tsa Lung meditation.

What is Tsa Lung Meditation?

In Tibetan Buddhist medicine, the subtle body is understood to be comprised of channels (tsa), and the wind/energy (lung or prana), and essence (tigle) that flow through those channels. Blockages in these channels cause imbalances in body systems because vital nutrients, oxygen, and blood don't flow properly. These blockages also cause energetic and mental blockages. Buddhist practice offers powerful methods to open these channels and make them clear and supple.

Practitioners of Tsa Lung meditation visualize *lung*, which is wind energy (chi) that moves down the center channel of the body to clear blockages and impurities as it continues on to permeate ever-smaller channels. Tsa Lung works intensively with the subtle body and the mind by combining breath-retention techniques with physical movements and visualizations. In this way, wind energy is moved throughout the body, allowing it to reach deep places and open more and more subtle channels. When the wind flows freely, the resulting energy *(prana)* can be used for self-healing or can be transferred to others.

Breath retention allows the movements in this practice to penetrate deeper into the body and open the most subtle chakras—which can only be opened with the breath. Movement alone isn't sufficient.

In general terms, Tsa Lung meditation involves performing five different exercises during which the practitioner inhales and brings mental focus and breath together to a particular chakra in the body. Additional breath is then inhaled and held as the practitioner does a specific movement designed to open the blockages and obscurations of that chakra. After releasing the breath, the practitioner rests in open awareness of the body's subtle qualities.

This physical practice is dynamic and powerful, and the breath retention makes it even more effective. It's important that we become aware of and train the breath. As we age, our breathing becomes more and more shallow and no longer reaches all parts of our body. Therefore, we need to relearn how to breathe deeply. When the breath flows freely, so does the mind. Working with the breath completely changes our thoughts. When we stop the breath, as in the Tsa Lung practice, we experience the deep stillness of our mind.

The Effects of Tsa Lung on the Body

Dr. William C. Bushell is an MIT-affiliated researcher in medical anthropology, and director of East-West Research for Tibet House in New York. Dr. Bushell wrote a scientific analysis of the processes occurring in Tsa Lung meditation. In his analysis, he speaks of the mild to moderate hyperthermia resulting from the practice, which kills bacteria and aids the body in healing.

"It's not entirely clear from a Western science perspective what the winds are, but the scientific evidence suggests to me and others that the meditative process involving winds includes increased local blood flow, metabolic activity, and oxygenation," he said.

Thomas K. Hunt, MD, under the sponsorship of the Institute of Noetic Studies in Petaluma, California, did research on the antibiotic properties of oxygenation in the blood and surrounding tissues resulting from doing Tsa Lung meditation. Dr. Hunt stated, "Our research showed that mental imagery directed to sites of the body—both superficial as well as deeper tissues—can, with practice, eventually lead to increased local blood flow, metabolic activity, and oxygenation. Such increases could, in principle, combat even powerful bacteria such as

Staphylococcus aureus, which not only can be the cause of gangrene but is now often resistant to antibiotics."

Renowned Yoga practitioner and Dzochen master Chögyal Namkhai Norbu (born in Tibet in 1938) states, "The most important part of all Tantric practices is Tsa Lung. When you do these practices in a perfect way, relaxing in the sensation of the pleasant feeling and staying in this presence, combining it with the visualization, you can obtain the following benefits: all the self-perfected, lhundrub qualities arise; also you automatically overcome attachment to food and you can easily integrate and stay in instant presence forever."

Instruction on Tsa Lung Meditation

For a guided Tsa Lung meditation, here's a good YouTube explanation:

https://www.youtube.com/watch?v=iMvVX6r5vz0

To see a practitioner do the meditation without dialogue, watch:

https://www.youtube.com/watch?v=3X3bwMSyyMk

Disclaimer: This practice isn't meant to replace conventional medical treatment, nor is it intended to diagnose, treat, cure, or prevent any disease.

Appendix 3: Brainspotting

by Cynthia Schwartzberg, LCSW

Introduction

As was identified in Chapter 3, some traumas or difficult past experiences can habitually collapse the wave function and create actions and reactions that limit our emotional response and negatively affect our health.

Sometimes a little extra help is needed to work these issues which is what this section deals with. The author, Cynthia, is a friend, she and I live in the same neighborhood and her office is right down the hall from my office. If you have questions about this approach, her website is included at the end of this article.

Brainspotting (BSP) is a trauma therapy developed by David Grand, PhD, in 2003. It's based on "where you look affects how you feel." So, if you're thinking of something depressing when you look to the right, it affects you differently than when you look to the left or the center. The BSP therapist uses this phenomenon to locate, focus, process, and release a wide range of emotional and body-based conditions.

During a BSP session, the client focuses on a specific issue. The therapist and client find a relevant eye position and body sensation. Once these are located, the client processes the issues using focused mindfulness. The eyes provide direct access to deep, subcortical brain activation, where much of trauma is embodied. The body sensation facilitates access to memories held in the body and brain. Focused mindfulness has been shown to help down-regulate (calm) the amygdala (the brain's alarm system).

251

How a Brainspotting Session Works

Trauma produces feelings of terror, horror, or helplessness. What we saw, heard, felt, or sensed during the traumatic event becomes our memory of it and part of our intrinsic autobiography. Our sense of self can be greatly altered by a traumatic event and, when we're faced with new experiences, this fragmented sense of self processes the experiences as if the past is in the present.

Trauma also threatens our psychological integrity, and we develop beliefs based on our survival instincts. Some of these beliefs refer to our basic sense of self and impact our interactions with others.

Our procedural memory, which is used for acquiring information and skills, becomes connected to the traumatic experience and perceives warnings of present danger. Many of these skills relate unconscious body functions connected to the traumatic experience as symptoms of the trauma.

In addition, the traumatic experience is hardwired into our nervous system and our memory. We repeatedly behave based on our expereince. During traumatic events, our neocortex shuts down, and we don't have access to our hippocampus—that part of our brain that helps us have a sense of time and space—or a coherent narrative of the experience in clear language. To have an explicit memory (cognitive intentional recollection) of an experience, we need executive functioning, which is an aspect of the neocortex.

Robert Scaer, MD says, "I would suggest that this unique narrowing, interruption, and corruption of perception of the present moment by past memory in traumatic stress is, in fact, what we define as dissociation." He refers to these states as dissociative capsules consisting of the body sensations, emotions, and thoughts that occurred at the time of the trauma.

And, he states, "Since endorphins were released in large amounts at the time of the threat and the freeze response that initiated the traumatic event, perceptions of the dissociative capsule will often be distorted and bizarre."

(http://www.traumasoma.com/excerpt1.html)

Traumatic experiences, therefore, are stored as implicit memories. We feel, think, and behave via our implicit memories, and these are expressed in behavior and strong feelings such as terror, depression, and anger without our having an understanding of these feelings. These implicit memories are without cognitive executive control.

Instead, we function from emotional reactions, drawing conclusions about situations based on past experiences. From this state, we don't have access to our logical mind to help us differentiate the present experience from the past. It's challenging to work with these experiences using cognitive based-therapies, because the body is frozen, in a sense, in time and space. By working with the mind and body together, we can help access unconscious material, gain a greater understanding of self, and bring the neocortex back on line with a subsequent return to homeostasis.

Example

I worked with a woman struggling with feelings of being rejected by her addicted mother, who couldn't properly care for her children. Growing up, the client became a "little mother" to her younger siblings. Understandably, she came to believe that, *"No one is ever there for me, and I don't know how to support myself."*

Though she was cognitively aware of her depression, she was unable to "come out of it" due to the resentment surrounding her mother's rejection. As a result of this resentment toward her mother, her self-perception was, *"I'm not capable."*

The Brainspotting work included a session in which she was able to find an eye position connecting to her sense of incapability, and, as she sifted through various memories, she felt the pain of the very young inner child who wasn't mothered as well as recalling things she was able to do. She left the session with hope and direction.

In a BSP session, it's typical for people to recall things they forgot, release feelings, and become more mindfully aware. We never know exactly where the work will go because of how the deep subcortical brain—in which the stored memories reside—works. Once some connections are made and the body releases held feelings, the neocortex comes back on board—often bringing awarenesses and new thoughts to consciousness. My patient took up some old, undeveloped talents and, over time, her sense of capability strengthened.

The brain and body connections continue processing after the BSP session, and people start to shift behavior so noticeably that it's typical for family or friends to comment on the positive changes.

The Role of the Therapist in Brainspotting

Brainspotting is regarded as a dual-attunement therapy. It harnesses the importance of the therapeutic relationship, which research has found as the key ingredient for any therapy to have a positive outcome. The therapist is focused on the client's neurobiology. While the client is engaged in focused mindfulness, the therapist is highly attuned to their neurobiology and creating a space for the client to allow their body's innate wisdom to heal itself. The therapist isn't directing the work nor telling the client about themselves. This allows for deep healing.

Dr. Scaer speaks about BSP as the preferred treatment for extinguishing the fear response created by a traumatic event. He says BSP does this by down-regulating the amygdala. He states, "It isn't just PNS (parasympathetic nervous system) activation that is facilitated, it is homeostasis."

(https://brainspotting.pro/page/what-brainspotting)

In other words, BSP helps restore balance and takes someone from a distorted sense of time and space to a more present, grounded state of being.

Dr. Scaer has this to say about the importance of dual attunement: "The attunement activates the mirror neurons between the cingulate and the OFC (orbital frontal cortex), creates an empathic environment, and inhibits the amygdala. This sacred, face-to-face empathic attunement is a critical environment for trauma therapy to work, just as it is in maternal-infant bonding...and this state of presence is essential for healing." (Scaer, 2012, p. 142)

How the Eyes Relate to the Process, and What Happens if a Client Has Trouble Seeing

Our eyes and brains are closely connected. Half of our brain is dedicated to vision, and we "see" with our brains as well as with our eyes. There's a part of our brain called the superior colliculus that helps us orient in our environment. Did you ever notice that when you're thinking of something, your eyes and/or body orient in a certain position to help you organize your thoughts? This is reflexive and provides signals to help us find the relevant eye position.

There are also other parts of our brain involved with vision that help us associate and label what we see. All of this is subcortical and plays an important part in how we store memories. The BSP process helps access this information. It's much more than visual sight.

More information about BSP and the brain areas affected during this process can be found in the *Medical Hypothesis Journal* article, "Brainspotting: Recruiting the midbrain for accessing and healing sensorimotor memories of traumatic activation," by Frank Corrigan MD and David Grand, PhD.

(https://www.cynthasis.com/resources/)

References:

www.cynthasis.com/

http://www.youtube.com/watch?v=xhUTEaNmCJg

http://www.traumasoma.com/excerpts/The%20Disscociation%20Capsule.pdf

Scaer, R. C. (2001). *The Body Bears the Burden*. New York: Haworth Medical Press.

Scaer, R.C.(2012) *8 Keys to Brain-Body Balance*. New York: W.W. Norton and Co.

Appendix 4: The Hell Realms

It's difficult to look at what's occurring in our world today. Everywhere we look, there's suffering—suffering that's happening not just on a human level but on a planetary level as well. It may seem like the pain of a starving child in Africa or a Blue Whale harpooned in the arctic seas has nothing to do with us, but, in fact, it does—not only on a spiritual plane but quite literally. Quantum physics and Buddhism both agree that all of life is interconnected and interdependent—everything depends on everything else. Even in our disconnected, distracted, technologically advanced age, we rely entirely on the health of the planet—its air, earth, and water—for our very lives. The Earth isn't an inert ball of dirt and rock. It's our living, breathing mother, and we've been treating her very poorly the last few centuries.

The concept of suffering is stated and thoroughly discussed in Buddhist doctrines that date back 2500 years. Generally speaking, Western and Eastern societies view suffering through different lenses. As Americans, when something goes awry, we immediately try to fix it and, oftentimes, assign blame. There's undoubtedly a resistance to the idea of suffering, and we rarely consider why we're suffering and if perhaps there's value in it, at least some of the time. On the other hand, Eastern societies perceive suffering as a normal part of life; when it occurs, we're encouraged to sit with it and acknowledge that it's happening. Trying to fix the issue to relieve the suffering usually doesn't come to mind. In this essay, I'll delve into the nature of suffering and its role on both the individual and planetary level. The Earth is suffering, and so are we.

The Buddhist Perspective on Suffering

One of the foundations of Buddhism is known as The Four Noble Truths. These are: 1) the truth of suffering, 2) the truth of the cause of suffering, 3) the truth of the end of suffering, and 4) the truth of the path that frees us from suffering. (O'brien, 2017) The First Noble Truth essentially states that suffering is part of life. The Second Noble Truth describes the root cause of our suffering—desire (and its reverse, aversion), which includes wanting something to be different than it is. Our attachment to what we desire or want to avoid is what causes us pain. The premise of the Second Noble Truth is that we're constantly unsatisfied and therefore searching for something more. In other words, we're never truly satisfied with what we have. In addition, we cling to things and phenomenon that are fleeting— which is everything. If you think about it, you realize that absolutely nothing in your environment stays the same. Not only does nothing last, it changes every moment. Even something that seems as permanent as a building or a mountain is constantly changing; we just can't see it. But we can clearly see how we, our loved ones, our friends, our enemies, our house, our dog—everything—is changing all the time. Yet, we cling to the illusion that if we accumulate enough money or wear the right clothes or do what someone wants us to do that we'll gain love and happiness that will last forever. This is a prime example of why we're almost never truly happy no matter how many material possessions we acquire.

The Three Kinds of Suffering

In Buddhist tradition, there are three kinds of suffering:

1. The suffering of suffering
2. The suffering of change
3. All-pervasive suffering of conditioning

The suffering of suffering is what we'd consider unavoidable suffering—the suffering inherent in living in a human body. The Buddhists identify four aspects of this type of suffering—the suffering of birth, old age, sickness, and death. This type of suffering also includes the pain we feel as a result of attachment—losing something we hold dear. Being forced to endure something we don't want or not achieving or getting what we do want are also conditions characterized as the suffering of suffering. A sutra (teaching of the Buddha) states: "What is the suffering upon suffering? It is that which is painful when arising, painful when remaining, and pleasant when changing."

The suffering of change refers to the fact that no matter how good or how bad any situation or state of mind that we find ourselves in, it won't last. As the Bible says, "All things must pass." Nothing stays the same, and this uncertainty causes anxiety—a form of mental suffering. To add to this, when a pleasurable situation ends, we often experience that same situation as painful. We need only think of anyone we loved who's now gone to know this kind of suffering. About the suffering of change, the Buddha said: "The suffering of change is that which is pleasant when arising, pleasant when remaining, but painful when ceasing."

Even a small, everyday change can make us feel stressed and uncomfortable, although often the change proves to be for our benefit. However, we usually realize this in retrospect. We hold the illusion that we can achieve a perfect and happy life if only we can stop things from changing. This, in a nutshell, is the foundation of all suffering.

The all-pervasive suffering of conditioning refers to the fact that whether, in this moment, we're experiencing pleasure, pain, or equanimity, our conditioning (that is, the fact that we're human) is setting us up for future suffering because we're living in illusion. If we're not aware—in the deepest sense—our present experiences must, inevitably, cause our future suffering. It can't be otherwise. The Buddha expresses this idea thus: "The suffering of being conditioned is not apparent when it arises, remains, or ceases, but it is still the cause of suffering."

If we were aware, we'd realize that everything we perceive as pleasure or pain is an illusion in the sense that it can't last. This is the meaning of the term "impermanence" in Buddhism. Everything that we perceive as "real" is constantly changing and, in that sense, is an illusion.

This brings us to the Third Noble Truth of Buddhism, which talks about the possibility of ending our suffering by becoming aware of our attachment to wanting things to be different than they are and recognizing how this makes us suffer. This isn't a theoretical idea that we simply try to adopt as a principle. When we're feeling pain of whatever kind (jealousy, anger, stress) and we look at ourselves honestly, we realize we're having that feeling because we want something we don't have, or we want something that's happening to us to stop.

The Buddha teaches that, through conscientious practice, our craving for what we think we need to be happy can be diminished. The Fourth Noble Truth of Buddhism delineates the path to the end of suffering. The path is comprised of eight areas of practice (called The Eightfold Path) that address every part of our lives and psyches. The Eightfold Path includes guidance on everything from ethical behavior (right conduct) to career (right livelihood) to living every day, in every moment, with mindfulness. (O'brien, 2017) Everything we say, do, and think is addressed by the Path. By diligently walking the Path, it's possible to end our suffering.

Buddhism also speaks of the hell realms, which comprise a variety of different kinds of suffering. These realms are described in elaborate and horrific detail, but they're largely meant to be symbolic of our states of mind rather than actual places.

Where Are the Hell Realms?

In traditional Buddhist teachings, the hell realms refer to the *bardos*, which are places the soul visits after death prior to rebirth in another form in this world. However, millions of people alive on earth now exist in a hell realm. Maybe you're one of those people. Stress is a hell realm, as are loneliness, regret, and worry. We all know people who suffer because they continuously obsess about something that happened in the past. The experience was over years ago, but the individual clings—willingly or unwillingly—to the emotion generated by that experience and, by doing so, creates their own hell realm. And, of course, there are people worldwide who are truly experiencing great physical and emotional pain in their lives right now in the form of war, famine, deportation, and starvation.

The concept of hell in Buddhism pertains not just to the *bardos* after death but to this world as well. Importantly, hell isn't a permanent destination. Through virtuous actions, beings can work their way to a better situation in their subsequent incarnations. Virtuous actions are characterized as those that show compassion for other beings and assist them in achieving their own enlightenment.

One striking belief in Buddhism is that the fire of the hell realms of *this* world is hotter than that of the hell realms beyond this world. This can be taken to mean that there's no suffering greater than anger, lust, greed, and ignorance. Another belief is that we're burning from more than ten different kinds of physical pain as well as mental agonies in the form of lust, hatred, illusion, sickness, decay, death, worry, lamentation, pain, melancholy, and grief. (Anson, 2011) Put simply, wherever there's suffering in this world, in whatever dimension, that place becomes a hell to those who suffer within it. That realm may be a city in the Middle East in which bombs are falling, or our own bed as we undergo the anguish of a disintegrating relationship. Both are hell realms. In the same way, wherever there's joy and kindness, that's a heaven to those who enjoy their worldly life within that emotional realm.

The take-home message about hell realms is that most—if not all—are of our own making. We create hellish environments in our own mind, but we're also creating external, physical hell realms that are not only killing the planet but all living beings—including us.

We Humans Are Creating Hell Realms on the Planet

Interdependence and interconnection—both of which are supported by quantum physics and Buddhism—means all beings (and perhaps every element in the universe) are influenced and affected by all other beings. This means that if an ant suffers, you suffer, as unlikely as that might seem at first blush. But if we ignore the suffering of an ant, we ignore our own suffering. This interrelatedness is easier to see among our fellow humans, but it extends to animals, trees, and every component of our planet.

There are many types of suffering we can do nothing about except to try to come to a place of accepting the suffering and transforming ourselves through it. This doesn't mean viewing the suffering as a good thing (although it sometimes can be) but acknowledging that it's our situation in that moment and seeing it with as much detachment as possible so as to be of as much benefit to ourselves and others as possible. An attitude of *"why me?"* will only disempower us and prevent us from seeing a way out of our suffering. There are many times when we can, indeed, find a way out by *being with* the suffering by not trying to escape it. We can see that if we're contributing to or even creating our own suffering (certainly envy, anger, and other such emotional hell realms are of our own creation), we can uncreate them through awareness and practice.

There are other forms of hell realms that we can do much to dispel—if we care to. These are the massive hell realms that we humans have created all over this planet. Those that affect our fellow human beings usually come to our minds first—wars, genocide, forced emigration, hate, bigotry, starvation, racism, sexism, and on and on—each and every one of them human-created. Quantum physics and Buddhism aside, we can no longer deny that everything in the world is connected. We see the effects of pollution arising thousands of miles from us on our air and water. We see what happens to the ecological balance if even one species goes extinct.

Let's explore some of these hell realms in detail and see both how they arose and what we can do about them.

Dead Zone in the Gulf of Mexico

There's a massive "dead zone" in the Gulf of Mexico. As it relates to oceans, a dead zone is defined as an area where there isn't enough oxygen in the water for marine life to survive. (Charles, 2017) These toxic areas of water are caused by large amounts of nutrient pollution spilling out from the Mississippi River. The pollution primarily consists of phosphorus and nitrogen, both of which are sourced from fertilizers that farmers use in the fields that drain into the massive watershed of the Mississippi, beginning thousands of miles upstream. When it rains, these fertilizers are washed into lakes and streams that feed into the Mississippi. (Charles, 2017) Once in the ocean, the phosphorus and nitrogen unleash blooms of algae that then die and decompose, all while absorbing an enormous amount of oxygen. This, in turn, leaves insufficient oxygen for other marine life.

The dead zone in the Gulf of Mexico is the size of the state of New Jersey—maybe not a huge area for a state but an enormous ecological disaster when we think of that much ocean as uninhabitable by marine life. You can see what the dead zone in the Gulf of Mexico looks like here:

http://www.npr.org/sections/thesalt/2017/08/03/541222717/the-gulf-of-mexicos-dead-zone-is-the-biggest-ever-seen

You can find an image showing a diver swimming in the dead zone here:

http://wkrg.com/2017/08/16/largest-dead-zone-in-the-u-s-located-in-the-gulf/

The water is so cloudy and dark with pollution that divers require flashlights to see underwater.

Islands of Plastic in the Pacific Ocean

Similar to the dead zone in the Gulf of Mexico, there's an area in the Pacific Ocean where unimaginably enormous amounts of plastic and debris have accumulated. This is known as the Great Pacific Garbage Patch. It extends from the west coast of the U.S. to Japan. Most of this garbage (the majority of which is plastic) isn't biodegradable, which means it will be remain there for eons.

Roughly 80% of the waste that makes up the Great Pacific Garbage Patch is created by land-based activities in the U.S. and Asia. (National Geographic, 2014) Scientists are unsure of just how much debris makes up the Great Pacific Garbage Patch, because it isn't just on the surface but in the deeper depths of the ocean as well. It's simply too deep and massive to measure. Of course, the trash in the Great Pacific Garbage Patch is immensely detrimental to marine life. Eventually, sea creatures that feed off algae won't have as much food. This will lead to less sustenance for larger marine mammals and, ultimately, to decreased availability of—and therefore increasingly expensive—seafood.

To learn more and view photos, visit here:

http://www.cookiesound.com/2011/08/the-great-pacific-garbage-patch/

E-Waste Everywhere

Another toxic entity that's dispersing throughout our oceans is e-waste. E-waste is defined as electronic products that are at the end or close to the end of their "useful life" or have been replaced by more technologically advanced versions and are therefore regarded as outdated. The most common forms of e-waste are computers, televisions, VCRs, stereos, copiers, and fax machines.

The components of most of these products can be reused, refurbished, or recycled. (CalRecycle, 2016) In Third World countries, people are plagued by poverty, which is often characterized not only by lack of resources but also by lack of education. What typically happens is that electronic trash is sent from developed countries to Third World countries such as Ghana, Nigeria, India, Pakistan, and China, to name a few. (McPhee, 2008) Much of e-waste recycling occurs in these Third World countries. The people who dismantle these-high tech gadgets are often unaware of the dangers involved in e-waste recycling and of how harmful the chemicals are to which they're exposed every day. Cadmium, arsenic, mercury, copper, lead, beryllium, chromium, zinc, barium, nickel, silver, and gold are all toxic elements used in the manufacture of electronic devices. (Toothman, 2008) When these devices are intact, there's no risk, but when they're dismantled, their hardware is exposed, or even if their casings are cracked, highly toxic gases are dispersed into the environment.

Some of the people in charge of electronic waste recycling in certain villages are under the impression they're helping other people by providing them with jobs. (McPhee, 2008) It's more likely, however, that the risks are known to those who own or operate electronic recycling operations, and they feel these impoverished, Third World people aren't as important as the almighty dollar. In addition, given the extreme poverty in many of these areas, it's likely that even if people know the health risks, they have no option but to keep working. We see the same thing in developed countries. Coal miners, refinery workers, and others are exposed to known carcinogens regularly but often these workers believe there are no other employment options.

The Reality We Create

You can find photos of a young Chinese girl disassembling an old CD, which puts her at great risk of breathing toxic gases that may later cause cancer and other photos depicting this problem here:

https://www.vqronline.org/vqr-gallery/china%E2%80%99s-e-waste-city

Culture of Carelessness

The bottom line is that allowing trash to taint our oceans, or e-waste to cause illness and death in our fellow human beings is the result of carelessness...and greed. There are entire countries—Germany, Japan, and Switzerland come to mind immediately—that are essentially devoid of free-range waste and garbage. These countries have a cultural ethic of not throwing trash along their roadways or into their wild places. They respect their land and their cities. This is a choice that the culture has made and maintained. There's nothing inherently German and Japanese about being tidy and clean. These cultures provide models that any of us could adopt.

I can't speak for other countries, but in the United States, I see a culture of carelessness. We toss trash anywhere, we accumulate junk in our garages and yards, and we disrespect our wild and beautiful places. Not all of us, of course, but enough of us that our country is a mess.

Our cities and landscapes are an obvious manifestation of this carelessness, but aren't we also careless of each other? Why do we allow so many of our citizens to suffer from lack of food and medical care in this country? We're a wealthy nation, and yet millions of American children don't have enough to eat, tens of thousands are homeless, and a growing percentage of Americans are living paycheck to paycheck (if they even receive a paycheck).

Greed is a part of this equation of carelessness, too. However, species we regard as much less "intelligent" than ourselves inherently know that the group can't survive without equal care of all its members. The mentality of scarcity doesn't exist for them and, as a result, there's not this drive to accumulate everything for oneself. Indigenous cultures know this as well. The vulnerable (children, the ill, and elders) are cared for by those more able. The young care for their elders knowing they, too, will be elders one day. There's a sense of perspective and balance. It seems modern people have lost all sense of that. Now the mantra is "more and more for me."

Buddhism teaches compassion for all beings—no matter how small, no matter whether we regard them as "pests" or even "undesirable" (spiders, snakes, cockroaches). This may seem like an archaic or quaint notion—to show compassion for an insect—but the motivation underlying it is essential for our continued existence on this planet. We're all connected. We need the bacteria living in our intestines to survive. We need the oxygen breathed out by trees. We need spiders to keep the numbers of mites and other creatures in check.

What we, so-called advanced humans, have forgotten is that the planet was in perfect balance until we started imposing our desires and aversions onto it. We like our hamburgers, so we mow down the rain forests to create more pastures for beef cattle—to our own detriment. America, especially, is a throwaway society. Each year, when the newest iPhone comes out, we throw away our perfectly good, "old" iPhone. We, as a culture, have created in ourselves a terminal craving for the newest, the best, the sexiest.

Which brings us back to suffering, and the causes of suffering—desire and aversion. The culture of most developed countries is all about consuming. Almost as soon as youngsters become cognizant of the world around them, they're exposed to the message that what's most vitally important to make them happy is having the newest toy and then the newest gadget and then the trendiest hairstyle. The goal is to surpass their friends in acquisitions and hipness. On the flip side, we belittle and bully those who aren't enrolled in being the coolest. And we've seen what happens to people—especially children—when they're bullied. They're plunged into such an excruciating hell realm that some of them take their own lives.

The First Step: Awareness of and Acceptance—Yes, Acceptance—of Suffering

In this endless pursuit of wanting, we create our own suffering, our own hell realms. It takes most of us the greater part of our lives to escape these hell realms, to realize that compassion, friendship, and caring for others are the true sources of happiness. As the Dalai Lama said, "If you want others to be happy, practice compassion. If you want to be happy, practice compassion."

So-called "enlightenment" isn't something devoted practitioners achieve after decades of meditation. Enlightenment is a process, and it's probably easier on us if we call it "awareness," because, ultimately, that's all it is—a continuous process of becoming more aware. When we're aware, we realize that our neighbor's suffering is our suffering, and her happiness brings us happiness.

Everyone experiences pain. It comes in many forms and is just a condition of life. What creates suffering is resisting that temporary condition, whatever it is. Becoming aware of how we can relieve that suffering should be the purpose of our life. In this regard, it's important to do a constructive discourse with yourself when you're suffering. By this, I don't mean comparing yourself to others, and acknowledging *"it could always be worse,"* and you should be grateful you have a roof over your head and food to eat. Comparing your life with that of people you perceive as less fortunate isn't a very deep form of understanding nor does it generate compassion. Awareness arises when we're able to step back, speaking metaphorically, and view our lives with perspective and compassion. We see that, in most cases, our suffering comes and goes.

If you're plagued by a particular and continuous source of suffering—creating a dead zone in your life—such as post-traumatic stress or guilt from past actions, meditation and the practice of mindfulness can be of tremendous help. You'll learn that you aren't your thoughts, and your thoughts aren't reality. This is a huge step in the awareness process. You may be feeling ashamed about something that you had no control over, or you may feel ashamed simply because an authority figure made you feel ashamed. Observing how your mind works, what thoughts arise, and what emotions are created by those thoughts often is sufficient to relieve the suffering caused by those mental constructs. You'll come to realize the source of what you're feeling and, by careful scrutiny of that cause, arrive at the root of your suffering.

Even if you've done something for which it's reasonable to feel guilt or shame or regret, that can be absolved by regarding yourself with compassion. We all have struggles and we all make mistakes—sometimes big mistakes. As Maya Angelou said, "I did then what I knew how to do. Now that I know better, I do better." With this attitude, we provide ourselves a path out of our suffering, just as the Buddha promised. When you take a step back, analyze any situation and your reaction to it, you might just be surprised at how the universe responds. You'll feel that expansion of your awareness, the blooming of compassion and forgiveness.

Mindfulness and Suffering

A famous Buddhist saying states, "Pain is inevitable, but suffering is optional." This sounds simplistic, but, if you truly understand what's being said, it can become a foundational truth of your life. We can't avoid pain, but we can avoid making ourselves suffer as a result of that pain, because suffering is entirely the result of desire or aversion—wanting or not wanting something. When we're not feeling well, we *desire* to feel better and to stop feeling bad. If, instead, we're able to accept the pain as a process our body is going through, we don't suffer as a result. Of course, this is no small feat. Humans are driven by their desires and aversions, and, when we're feeling miserable, we want that to stop. But if we're able to step back and view ourselves as perfect spirits inhabiting a fallible body, if we're able to do this even for a moment, we can see the difference between pain and suffering. In this way, we inch our way toward a more joyful life.

References:

CalRecycle (2016) *What is E-Waste?* Retrieved from: http://www.calrecycle.ca.gov/electronics/whatisewaste/

Charles, Dan (2017) NPR. Food For Thought. *The Gulf of Mexico's Dead Zone is the Biggest Ever Seen* Retrieved from: http://www.npr.org/sections/thesalt/2017/08/03/541222717/the-gulf-of-mexicos-dead-zone-is-the-biggest-ever-seen

HowStuffWorks.com. <http://electronics.howstuffworks.com/everyday-tech/e-waste.htm> 15 September 2017.

McPhee, Glynnis. (2008) *Field Notes*. Peter Essick Interview. National Geographic.Retrievedfrom:http://ngm.nationalgeographic.com/2008/01/high-tech-trash/essick-field-notes

National Geographic (2014) *Great Pacific Garbage Patch* Retrievedfrom:https://www.nationalgeographic.org/encyclopedia/great-pacific-garbage-patch/

O'Brien, Barbara. "The Four Noble Truths of Buddhism." ThoughtCo, Aug. 4, 2017, thoughtco.com/the-four-noble-truths-450095.

Toothman, Jessika. HowStuffWorks (2017) *How E-waste Works*Retrievedfrom:http://electronics.howstuffworks.com/everyday-tech/e-waste1.htm

About the Author

Hi. I'm Warren Cargal, husband, father of an incredible young man, avid cyclist, board-certified Acupuncturist with 20+ years of experience, and author of two books:

Your Mitochondria: Key to Health & Longevity, and

The Reality We Create: The Influence of Beliefs and Consciousness on Our Health and Longevity.

I believe that all of us deserve a healthy, vital life and that we have the potential to create that for ourselves.

My fundamental approach to help you achieve a healthy, creative life is to support you in questioning long-held beliefs about the root causes of chronic disease or aging. There is ample evidence which shows that the greatest health transformations unfold when you address the root cause. What you may not realize is how vital a role you play in your own health, and in improving it.

At my clinic, Acupuncture Atlanta, my team and I work every day to empower people who are dealing with chronic disease conditions. Over and over again, we find that healing can sometimes be as simple as lifestyle interventions that are often ignored by mainstream medicine.

If you're a practitioner or health coach, my books offer you the latest research on the driving forces of chronic disease conditions, aging, and how our consciousness creates our health and creativity.

Thanks for reading the book!

Email me if you have questions: wcargal9@acuatlanta.net

44306740R00150

Made in the USA
Columbia, SC
19 December 2018